Fingerprints of God

RECOGNIZING GOD'S TOUCH ON YOUR LIFE

JENNIFER ROTHSCHILD

LifeWay Press®
Nashville, Tennessee

Published by LifeWay Press®
© 2005 • Jennifer Rothschild
Third printing September 2006

ISBN 1-4158-2088-0

This book is course CG-1099 in the Women's Enrichment category of the
        Christian Growth Study Plan.
Dewey Decimal Classification Number: 231.7
Subject Headings: GOD \ SPIRITUAL LIFE

Cover: Jon Rodda, Art Direction; Susan Browne, Design;
Image Source, child photo; Digital Vision, rain photo

Unless otherwise indicated, all Scripture quotations are from the Holy Bible, New International
        Version, © Copyright 1973, 1978, 1984 by International Bible Society.
Scripture quotations identified KJV are from the King James Version.
Scripture quotations identified NASB are from the New American Standard Bible, Copyright ©
        1960, 1962, 1963, 1968, 1971, 1972, 1973, 1975, 1977, 1995 by the Lockman
        Foundation. Used by permission. (www.lockman.org)
Scripture quotations identified NLT are from the Holy Bible, New Living Translation,
        Copyright © 1996. Used by permission of Tyndale House Publishers, Inc.,
        Wheaton, IL 60189 USA. All rights reserved.
Scripture quotations identified The Message are from The Message. Copyright © 1993, 1994,
        1995, 1996, 2000, 2001, 2002. Used by permission of NavPress Publishing Group.
Scripture quotations identified AMP are from The Amplified Bible, copyright © 1954, 1958,
        1962, 1964, 1965, 1987 by The Lockman Foundation. Used by permission.
        (www.lockman.org)
Scripture quotations identified NKJV are from the New King James Version. Copyright © 1979,
        1980, 1982, Thomas Nelson, Inc., Publishers.
Scripture quotations identified CEV are from the Contemporary English Version
        Copyright © 1991, 1992, 1995 by American Bible Society. Used by permission.
Scripture quotations identified NCV are from The Holy Bible, New Century Version,
        copyright © 1987, 1988, 1991 by W Publishing Group, Nashville, TN 37214.
        Used by permission.
Scripture quotations identified ASV are from The American Standard Version.

All hymns and their stories are taken from the The One Year Book of Hymns, ed. Robert K. Brown
and Mark R. Norton (Wheaton, Ill., Tyndale House Publishers, Inc., 1995)

To order additional copies of this resource, write to LifeWay Church Resources
Customer Service; One LifeWay Plaza; Nashville, TN 37234-0013; fax (615) 251-5933;
phone toll free (800) 458-2772; e-mail customerservice@lifeway.com;
order online at www.lifeway.com; or visit the LifeWay Christian Store serving you.

Printed in the United States of America

Leadership and Adult Publishing
LifeWay Church Resources; One LifeWay Plaza
Nashville, TN 37234-0175

Contents

About the Author

All of God's children bear His fingerprints. For Jennifer Rothschild, God's touch has been her guide and shelter.

At the age of 15, Jennifer was diagnosed with a rare, degenerative eye disease that would eventually steal her sight. It was more than a turning point for the Miami, Florida native. Her dreams of becoming a commercial artist and cartoonist faded. Words and music have replaced her canvas and palette.

Through her spiritual depth and down-to-earth style, Jennifer weaves music, illustrations, and biblical truth to help people find contentment, walk with endurance, and celebrate the ordinary. Through her story-telling and wit, they look beyond circumstances and experience God's grace in adversity.

In addition to this study, Jennifer is the author of the trade books *Fingerprints of God* (formerly, *Touched By His Unseen Hand*) and *Lessons I Learned in the Dark,* and the popular Bible study *Walking by Faith.* Along with her writing and speaking ministry, Jennifer is an accomplished songwriter and recording artist with six albums to her credit—including *Walking by Faith: The Music Captured Live, Along the Way,* and others. Jennifer partnered with worship leader Travis Cottrell to record their arrangement of "He Touched Me" as a backdrop for this study. She also co-founded and publishes a popular online magazine for women, WomensMinistry.NET.

Jennifer and her husband, Philip, live in Springfield, Missouri, with their sons, Clayton and Connor. Jennifer enjoys nature walks, theme parks, and riding a bicycle built for two.

Other Contributors

Karen True fell in love with studying God's Word during her college years, so contributing to this study has been a great personal delight.

Karen holds a degree in marketing from Southwest Missouri State University, and her background in corporate and not-for-profit finance provides both personal and practical insight to her writing. Along with her family, she is actively involved at Second Baptist Church in Springfield, Missouri where she serves as Women's Minister and Bible teacher. Karen is married to Gerry and they have a daughter, Madeleine and a son, Mason. Karen has partnered with Jennifer on previous projects, including *Lessons I Learned in the Dark, Walking by Faith,* and the trade version of *Fingerprints of God: Recognizing the Touch of God on Your Life.*

As the deadline for this manuscript drew near, Karen was directly touched by God's great unseen hand. Diagnosed with thyroid cancer, she underwent successful surgery and radiation. The experience has become for Karen yet another personal encounter with God's perfect timing, love, healing, mercy, and of course, His touch.

Susan A. Lanford is a writer and speaker on parenting, marriage, spiritual growth, and spiritual perspectives in healthcare. She has degrees from Texas Christian University and Southwestern Seminary. Her family is active in Second Baptist Church, Little Rock, where she teaches in the student and women's Bible study ministries and facilitates discipleship groups. Susan and her husband, Randy, have three children, Jonathan, Jay, and Bethany, and a precious daughter-in-law, Becky.

Introduction

God taught this study's truths to me firsthand. It startles me to know God's touch separates me from all other created beings. This study shattered my view of a heavenly hand that merely spends its energies whipping up majestic waves and hurling bolts of lightning across the sky's dark canvas. My eyes welled with tears as I felt the intimate touch of a Father who knows me personally. I've been brought to my knees in sheer humility and gratitude as I've been touched afresh by the nail-scarred hand that clutches me within its redemptive grasp. Now I understand that God's hand rests steadily on my shoulder as He guides me through pathways that I can't navigate alone.

I'm thrilled and thankful you've chosen to join me for this study. I have felt the extraordinary touch of God on my life and long for you to feel the wonder and awe of His marvelous touch, too. I've been praying you will recognize God's mighty but gentle hand and feel the warmth of His touch.

Although it's not skin on skin, God's touch is always personal. Over the next six weeks you'll learn to be sensitive to His touch. Commit with me to finish each day's assignment. Listen to God and follow His direction to further study. Use note cards to record Scriptures to remember. You might be surprised to feel God's touch through this simple discipline. Choose one person in your group to pray for and encourage. Maybe you can help each other memorize Scripture! You and your partner may choose to do specific Touch Points together each week. This relationship will allow you to experience and extend God's touch through fellowship and Christian growth.

Friend, would you commit to journal during this study? Your journal should reflect your personality. If you're crafty, you might like to make your own, but notebook paper will do just fine! The journal's should help you recognize and record all God teaches you and how you experience His presence. Use this invaluable tool to record answered prayer as well as needs in your life and in your prayer partner's life. Don't miss the blessing of recording the lessons God teaches you along the way.

I hope God will use this study in your head, heart, and hands. I've asked Him to write these truths on your mind so you can understand and have His wisdom and revelation. I've asked Him to plant the truth in your soul where your emotions are engaged. I've prayed your very own hands will extend the touch you receive, and I've given you examples in the weekly Touch Points. So my friend, open the eyes of your heart. You're about to see God's fingerprints everywhere you look.

"The works of his hands are faithful and just; all his precepts are trustworthy."
Psalm 111:7

Listening Guide

The fingerprints of God serve two purposes in our lives: They ...

1. reveal His _____.

2. remind us of His _____.

The touch of God ...

- _____ us (Matt. 14:22-31).

- brings us _____ (Matt. 17:1-7).

- blesses and _____ us (Matt. 19:13-15).

- _____ what we lost (Matt. 20:29-34).

- is _____ (Mark 1:40-42).

- is _____ and intimate (Mark 7:31-35).

- _____ and _____ when we cannot see (Mark 8:22-25).

- _____ us (Mark 9:14-27).

- is a touch of _____ (Luke 22:49-51).

In this study we will:

1. _____ God's touch.

2. _____ God's touch.

3. _____ God's touch (Matt. 25:31-40).

Fingerprints of God

"God saw all that he had made, and it was very good" (Gen. 1:31). All God's creation reflected His personal goodness. The Apostle Paul echoed this divine contemplation when he pointed out that God's marvelous visible creation clearly displays His even more marvelous invisible qualities. God designed the observable world to help us envision with our hearts what we cannot see with our eyes.

Samuel Longfellow, the lesser known but equally poetic brother of Henry Wadsworth Longfellow, showed he caught this kind of glimpse of the invisible God. Samuel loved the seashore. He often surveyed the glorious ocean with its mighty surges, its mysterious depths, and utter vastness. Perhaps the sight of a delicate coral reef left him awash in God's tenderness and beauty. A dancing sea horse or squirming jelly fish likely brought to mind God's astonishing creativity. The crashing waves and thunderous billows clearly expressed God's majesty and power.

I wonder if Longfellow beheld a different image of majesty when he glanced at his own reflection during his walk along the puddled shore. His prose resonates with the words of the Apostle Paul from centuries earlier: "Since the creation of the world God's invisible qualities … have been clearly seen, being understood from what has been made" (Rom. 1:20).

Imagine that you too are at seaside and consider this heavenly object lesson. If you'll look with your heart's eyes, you'll easily observe God's splendor there. You'll distinguish His unbounded influence and His unspoiled law. You're even likely to notice, maybe for the very first time, that we are represented there too. For we are His very image and have been imprinted with His unmistakable likeness.

God of the Earth, the Sky, the Sea

God of the earth, the sky, the sea,
Maker of all above below,
Creation lives and moves in Thee,
Thy present life through all doth flow.

Thy love is in the sunshine's glow,
Thy life is in the quickening air;
When lightnings flash and storm
    winds blow,
There is Thy power; Thy law is there.

We feel Thy calm at evening's hour,
Thy grandeur in the march of night;
And when the morning breaks in power,
We hear Thy word, "Let there be light!"

But higher far, and far more clear,
Thee in man's spirit we behold;
Thine image and Thyself are there,
Th' indwelling God, proclaimed of old.

Touch Stones

"By the word of the Lord were the heavens made,
    their starry host by the breath of his mouth.
For he spoke, and it came to be;
    he commanded, and it stood firm." Psalm 33:6,9

"My salvation and my honor depend on God;
    he is my mighty rock, my refuge." Psalm 62:7

DAY ❀ ONE

Handcrafted

Have you stood before a magnificent ocean, feeling its majestic power and misty thunder as it slaps the shoreline and drags the sand into its lair? I have, and when I do, I feel very small. My size compared to the vast ocean is not unlike the miniscule size of the earth compared to the vast expanse of the heavens.

Consider just our own Milky Way galaxy which contains over a hundred billion stars. Its diameter is 100,000 light years. Comparing its vastness to Earth's smallness, it's remarkable the Bible even mentions our tiny planet. Genesis 1:1 points out this comparison when it says, "In the beginning God created the heavens and the earth."

Consider how God accomplished creation. Complete the following from Psalm 33:6,9:

"By the _____ of the Lord were the heavens made,

their starry host by the _____ of his _____.

For he _____, and it came to be;

he _____, and it stood firm."

What did God use to create the universe? (This is not a trick question.)
❏ His voice   ❏ His hands   ❏ evolution

Read the creation account in Genesis 1:3-26. What does the fact that God spoke all creation into being tell you about Him?

_____

How amazing that God could have used any means to initiate creation, yet He simply spoke and it appeared. But even more amazing is that when He created man He didn't use His voice; He used something far more personal.

Read Genesis 2:7,21-22. What did God use to create man and woman?

❑ His voice   ❑ His hands   ❑ a subcontractor

The universe began with God's spoken word. All the grandeur, majesty, and wonder of a creation beyond our comprehension began with His voice. In Genesis 1:3 God said, "Let there be light." From there, He spoke His vast creation into existence. Planets and stars. Mountains and oceans. Forests and animals. Birds and sea creatures. Towering trees and tiny flowers. All creation was initiated by God's word. All except man.

God could have spoken us into existence, too, but He chose to use His hands. His touch separates us from all other created things.

Does God, a Spirit, truly have hands as we have hands? I'll leave that one for the theologians. I only know that Scripture differentiates the way God formed man and woman from how He created every other thing. It wasn't business as usual. I don't know exactly how He did it, but I do know a special touch was involved.

Can you wrap your mind around that idea? Read Isaiah 40:22. Imagine we're standing at the edge of the Atlantic, in the shadow of Mount Everest, or on the floor of the Grand Canyon. Does the magnificence of creation make you feel like a grasshopper? Describe how you feel in relation to the surrounding grandeur.

_____

_____

David felt the same way. He was merely a boy, lowest in the family pecking order, when the prophet Samuel proclaimed David would one day rule Israel as king. He must have felt ridiculously undersized when King Saul sought to dress him in the royal armor to fight the giant Goliath. Years later, as a middle-aged king himself, the gentle psalmist must have felt the frailty of his stature as the man after God's own heart broke God's heart by choosing Bathsheba rather than battle.

I wonder what life was like for David as a shepherd boy resting in the cleft of a rock and plucking his harp strings in the cool of the evening. Perhaps he looked across the surrounding Judean hills at dusk and thought of his smallness. Perhaps he gazed into the soft light of a star-blanketed sky and once again felt his size.

"The LORD has sought out a man after his own heart."

1 Samuel 13:14

What amazed David about the grandeur of God's handiwork (Psalm 8:3-4)?

_____

Does the fact that God is mindful of us blow your mind? It does mine. We seem such a small part of God's creation. Yet, He esteems us and honors us above all His handiwork.

According to Psalm 8:5-6, what does God do for us as the crowning jewel of His creation?

1. _____ 3. _____

2. _____ 4. _____

Based on these four things that display God's honoring touch on your life, write a prayer of thankfulness.

_____

_____

_____

DAY ❀ TWO
Broken Yet Valuable

During my college years, a friend of mine gave me a beautiful Lladró® porcelain figurine. Her slender lines were accentuated by a graceful hat and a vase of flowers. For the first seven years of our marriage, this delicate figurine moved from city to city and from home to home. It was one of my most treasured possessions.

One fateful afternoon, though, our four-year-old son was playing a game of hide-and-seek near the table where the figurine stood. A bump of the table sent her to the floor, chipping the tips of the petals on her flowers. We glued her dainty pieces back together as best we could, but her bouquet was never the same.

Many years have passed. Another city, another home. My beautiful Lladró® has followed, and she still finds her home in our living room. I often wonder why I value her so—why she has a place of honor on my mantle. She's flawed. She's no longer smooth. She's no longer perfect. She's surely lost all monetary value.

Perhaps I value her because she reminds me of someone I know—me. I, too, am broken and imperfect. I've lost some of my slender lines. My bouquet has been chipped. We're all broken and flawed. But we are still of value because Someone values us. God loves us and positions us in a place of honor. He continually honors us by the way He treats us. In fact, from the beginning, we see the heart of God fixed on us, His creation.

The Bible shows the value God places on us. He loves us and honors us with His touch. Walk with me through books of the Bible. This is a journey I can't wait to share with you. Every time I read it, I get teary-eyed when I recognize my value to God.

- In Genesis, He fashions you with His hands.
- In Exodus, He gives you freedom and deliverance.
- In Leviticus, He gives you access to Himself.
- In Numbers, He builds cities of refuge to protect you.
- In Deuteronomy, He guides you with His protective hand.
- In Joshua, He honors you with His divine purpose.
- In Judges, He shows you mercy in spite of repeated failures.
- In Ruth, He values you by bringing you into His family.
- In 1 and 2 Samuel, He makes the insignificant significant.
- In 1 and 2 Kings, He honors you by His faithfulness.
- In the Chronicles, He makes your prayer powerful, granting you success.
- In Ezra and Nehemiah, He allows you to return to Him and gives you tools to rebuild all that is broken.
- In Esther, He gives you purpose and makes you royalty.
- In Job, He restores you and shows Himself strong on your behalf.
- In Psalms, He calls you close and encourages you to sing in His presence.
- In Proverbs, He reveals His wisdom to you.
- In Ecclesiastes, He gives meaning to meaninglessness.
- In Song of Solomon, He draws you to run after Him, the Lover of your soul.
- In Isaiah, He reveals the Savior to you.
- In Jeremiah and Lamentations, He sees your tears and gives you hope.
- In Ezekiel and Daniel, the Sovereign Lord joins you in the midst of the fire.
- In Hosea, God pursues you to buy you back.
- In Joel, He blesses you when you repent.
- In Amos, He bears your burdens.
- In Obadiah, He keeps His covenant to you.
- In Jonah, He honors you by using imperfect man to fulfill His own perfect plan.
- In Micah, He invites you to walk humbly with Him.
- In Nahum, He comforts you.
- In Habakkuk, He brings you from lowliness to high places.
- In Zephaniah, He sings over you with great joy.
- In Haggai, God Himself makes His dwelling with you.

- In Zechariah, God reveals His plans for your future and assures you of His coming.
- In Malachi, God shows that you can't out-give Him as He pours out His blessing.
- In the Gospels God puts on human flesh to seek and save you.
- In Acts, He pours out His Spirit on you.
- In Romans, He works all things for your good!
- In the letters to the Corinthians, He pulls you from error, teaches you the way of love, and points you toward unseen realities.
- In Galatians, He sets you free!
- In Ephesians, He lavishes you with the riches of grace.
- In Philippians, He gives you victory and joy.
- In Colossians, we are rooted and strengthened in Him—and overflow with thankfulness.
- In letters to Thessalonian churches, He honors you by giving you a future hope.
- In letters to Timothy, He offers you counsel and encouragement.
- In Titus, He equips you for good works.
- In Philemon, He turns your slavery into brotherhood.
- In Hebrews, He invites you to come boldly before His throne.
- In James, He teaches you practical religion.
- In 1 and 2 Peter, He gives you victory over suffering.
- In the three epistles of John, He assures you of eternity and invites you to walk in His light, life, and love.
- In Jude, God tenderly keeps you from falling and values you so highly that He Himself presents you faultless before His own throne.
- And then in Revelation, He receives you as His beloved and treasured bride.

Through every book of the Bible God communicates your value. Read the following verses from Psalm 139 and write in first person the evidence of your worth to God.

Verse 1 <u>Lord, You've paid attention to me, and You really understand me.</u>

Verse 2 <u>You're familiar with my schedule and my world.</u>

Verse 3 _____

Verse 4 _____

Verse 5 _____

Verses 9-10 _____

Verse 13 _____

Verse 14 _____

Verse 16 _____

You are the reason God established and kept His covenant. You are the reason He grew a tree that became a cross.

What does 2 Peter 3:9 indicate about your value to God?

_____

Ultimately, value is determined by price paid. If Jesus Christ saw fit (and He did) to pay the ultimate price for you, I'd say that He thinks you're very valuable. Even when we don't feel valuable, we still are valuable. Even when we don't feel noticed, God's eyes never leave us. Even when we don't feel His touch, our lives reflect His hand. Even when darkness surrounds us, we can be sure that God sees us.

DAY ❧ THREE

Seen by God

A woman who lived centuries ago understood what it means to be seen by God. She was a simple Egyptian slave girl named Hagar. When I asked my business-professor husband about the story of Hagar, he proceeded to explain to me how a clever entrepreneur created and marketed a pair of leisure pants for the American male.

Well, I was not exactly thinking of that Hagar. But at least he didn't mention the portly cartoon Viking featured in the comics! These days, this lady from the pages of Scripture seems destined to play second fiddle to a cartoon character and a pair of pants.

Read about Hagar in Genesis 16. Choose five words to describe her life and situation:

1. _____   4. _____

2. _____   5. _____

3. _____

According to Genesis 16:6, how was Hagar treated?

_____

Obviously, Hagar was mistreated, so she ran away. That's what I would have done, too. That's what we do when we feel devalued or dishonored. We may not physically hit the road, but we do run away—emotionally and spiritually—from those who hurt us. Most of us run to escape. We run to find a place to feel more significant or valued. Hagar ran to the wilderness to escape Sarai's abuse and the harshness of her circumstances.

Today, some of us run to anonymous relationships with fellow chatters on the internet. Some run to bottles of pills, shopping malls, the refrigerator, or other destructive habits. Some run to more socially-acceptable escape hatches. One I know well is marked *Perfectionism*. Another is marked *Gossip*. Think about where you run when you want to feel valuable. Think about where you end up.

From what or whom do you run away? _____

Where do you run to escape? _____

When Hagar ran, she ended up by a spring. Can't you just see her? I imagine she collapsed by the spring out of pure physical and emotional exhaustion. Do you think she wept from the pain that she'd never really been loved or valued? I wonder if her tears were interrupted as she heard someone speak her name.

"Hagar."

The voice she heard by the spring was different—like no voice she had ever heard before. "Hagar, servant of Sarai, where have you come from, and where are you going?" (Gen. 16:8). It was the voice of the angel of the Lord. The angel revealed that not only did God see this young woman, but He also took note of her circumstances.

Hagar may rarely (if ever) have felt noticed or cared about—and now none other than the God of the universe stooped low enough to see her, craned His neck just to hear her cry, and sent to her the angel of the Lord just to speak her name.

How did Hagar respond to God (v. 13)?

_____

How do you think you would respond to God in a similar situation?

_____

Read Psalm 33:13-15. Write in the margin the words that show God's eyes are on you.

How does it make you feel to know God sees you? Underline the phrase in each set that best describes God watching you.

parole officer or secret admirer   suspicious neighbor or protective father

jealous coworker or adoring fan   intolerant boss or attentive mentor

Read Matthew 10:29-31. Why does God watch you? _____

It should startle our souls, just as it did Hagar's, when we realize that God truly sees us. He knows our circumstances, and He honors and values us above all creation.

According to Psalm 62:7, where does your honor come from? _____

Your honor and value come neither from what you do nor from others' opinions. You are honored because God has touched you with His presence, promise, and provision. When His eyes look on you, you are bathed in honor.

DAY ❁ FOUR
Wear the Crown

As Connor pried lids off of his new Play-Doh® the aroma filled the room. Combining all four colors, he fashioned a creation only a three-year-old architect could design. Finally, he gasped with awe and pride. "Mommy, it's so beautiful!"

"Tell me why it's so beautiful," I probed. "I used all the colors," he answered, "then, I smushed it in my hands." Since I thought he was finished, I began to compliment his artwork. He quickly interrupted me, "But Mommy, it was my fingerprints that made it the most beautiful."

Connor's creation looked a lot like us. Like Hagar, we've been poked and dented, yet shaped by a loving Creator whose watches over us. As we thumb through the photo album of our lives, we can't help but see His fingerprints.

God's touch makes us valuable. We sometimes feel more awkward than attractive, but we are marked with our Creator's loving and tender fingerprints. He has crowned us with honor, but we fixate on our own flaws and often don't recognize His touch.

Do you wear God's crown of honor? Circle the letter that most closely matches your response to each of the following statements.

	Never	Sometimes	Often	Always
I feel very good about myself.	A	B	C	D
I am confident.	A	B	C	D
I have purpose.	A	B	C	D
I feel like I measure up.	A	B	C	D
I can accept that God cares about me.	A	B	C	D
I can handle being wrong.	A	B	C	D
I take criticism well.	A	B	C	D

If you picked mostly A's and B's, fret not my royal sister, but thou art not wearing the crown of honor God gavest you. If you picked mostly B's and C's, you've put on His crown of honor, but you're not completely convinced that it fitteth. If you picked mostly C's and D's, thou art either dishonest or thou dost wear thy crown well.

God intends for us to be the crowning jewel of His creation. He made us in His image to reflect and enjoy His glory. Let's see what His glory looks like.

Underline the words below that reveal God's honor and authority.

👑 "The eternal God is your refuge" (Deut. 33:27).

👑 "Now to the King eternal" (I Tim. 1:17).

👑 "God, the blessed and only Ruler" (I Tim. 6:15).

These titles reflect God's glory, honor, and authority. Since we are made in His image, we too reflect His attributes.

Circle the words in the following Scriptures that reveal our honor and authority.

👑 "You are a chosen people, a royal priesthood, a holy nation" (I Pet. 2:9).

👑 "You made him ruler over the works of your hands; you put everything under his feet" (Ps. 8:6).

👑 "He has made everything beautiful in its time. He has also set eternity in the hearts of men" (Ecc. 3:11).

Scripture establishes that we reflect the glory of God, but sometimes we don't experience the joy of being an heir. We don't feel as if we have dominion, and sometimes we get short-sighted and forget that we're made for eternity. I know how you feel. You and I often do not wear with authority the crown that is rightfully ours. Why is that? I have a feeling we'll find out why if we look to Eve.

Read Genesis 3:4-6.

More than handing out forbidden fruit, Eve also gave away our glory, honor, and authority. Eve took the fruit because she'd been tempted and deceived.

Whom did Satan convince Eve she would be like if she ate the fruit?

❑ Adam   ❑ the Lord God   ❑ the crafty serpent

Our image reflects God's image, and we share His honor. He shares His authority with us. When Eve was tempted to become like God, she already bore His likeness and didn't recognize it. Do you? Think about that. We'll pick up this thought and our crowns again tomorrow.

DAY ❀ FIVE
Stay on the Mantle

Yesterday, we considered that we are all created in the image of God, yet we don't always reflect His image or wear His crown of honor. You might struggle with this as I do. Many of us haven't recognized God's fingerprints on our lives. If we're not living according to the honor and authority we've been given, let's try and understand why. As we saw, Eve was deceived. To attain something she already had, she gave her authority away and lost it all. Perhaps we don't wear the crown because we're deceived also.

Even though you weren't physically in Eden that day, you were in the garden too. You handed over your honor and authority along with Adam and Eve. Here's how we know:

Read I Corinthians 15:22. What did we receive through Adam? _____

When Adam and Eve sinned, they traded life for death. They turned over their authority and honor from God, the giver of life, to Satan, the full representation of death.

Read the following Scripture phrases to see the image of Satan's counterfeit honor and authority. Then find the crowns (♔) on pages 17-18. Write the underlined words in the appropriate columns.

God	Man (Adam and Eve)	Satan
♔ _____	♔ _____	♔ "prince of this world" (John 16:11)
♔ _____	♔ _____	♔ "god of this age" (2 Cor. 4:4)
♔ _____	♔ _____	♔ "ruler of the kingdom of the air" (John 16:11)

God did not give Satan glory or authority. This rightfully belonged to man; therefore, only man could abdicate it. Basically, we handed Satan the ability to counterfeit God's image.

Suppose a generous father bought a beautiful new car for his daughter's 16th birthday. The grateful daughter cruised around town enjoying her wheels. One day, though, a sly talkin', leather wearin', shower needin' thug talked her into signing the back of the title. Along with the title went her ownership of the car—lost forever. The only way to get the car back was for her Daddy to purchase it again. And her Daddy did. I hope this story sounds familiar.

The daughter did not have the means to buy back her car except through the help of her father. Nor do we have the means to regain our relinquished authority except through the provision of our heavenly Father.

Explain what Matthew 28:18 and Ephesians 1:19-22 say about Jesus' authority.

_____

Now, let me tell you in my own words. Jesus is the ultimate authority. He's the embodiment of authority. He's the essence of authority. He is above all!

That means that He alone has the means to buy back the authority we gave away. Though we lost our authority in the garden, we regained it through the cross. Jesus, the God Man, stamped out Satan's authority once and for all when the stone was rolled away.

What word in each of these verses describes the transaction Jesus made for us?

I Corinthians 6:20 _____   Titus 2:14 _____

Revelation 5:9 _____

First Peter 1:18-19 says we were not purchased with silver or gold but with Christ's precious blood. Because Jesus has ultimate authority and is worthy to redeem us, He alone can restore through the cross what we lost in the garden. Your value, authority, honor, and very salvation are from God (Ps. 62:7). So put on your crown. Stop giving Satan the title. You have authority because you have been bought with a price. Satan is now subject to you. Truth is the key to exercising your authority. Look again at your price tag. Like my Lladró your petals may be broken, your lines may not be so slender, your crown may be tilted; but you still a hold a place of honor on the mantle of God's heart.

"'I have given you authority to trample on snakes and scorpions and to overcome all the power of the enemy; nothing will harm you. However, do not rejoice that the spirits submit to you, but rejoice that your names are written in heaven'" (Luke 10:19-20).

"You, dear children, are from God and have overcome them, because the one who is in you is greater than the one who is in the world" (I John 4:4).

God's touch honors you. How can you leave His fingerprints?

Touch Point

The women's ministry in my church took a group to our local domestic violence shelter. The residents received manicures, gifts, a home-cooked meal, and a few hours of fun. The purpose was simply to communicate, "You matter!" Someone in your life needs this message also. What can you do to acknowledge someone, not for anything they do or have done, but just because he or she exists? Give the gift of your time and let someone be the center of your attention this week. When you do, you'll leave God's fingerprints on his or her life.

Listening Guide

The LORD God _____ into a woman the rib which He had

taken from the man (Gen. 2:22, NAS).

God _____ to make man and woman with His _____.

We are honored by …

  • His _____.

  • His _____.

When God sees you, He sees _____, so _____ Him.

We are honored by …

  • His touch.

  • His gaze.

  • His _____.

A Touch of Intimacy

Worn out by tuberculosis and asthma at age 54, Henry Francis Lyte remarked, "It is better to wear out than to rust out." He had pastored faithfully over two decades in a poor church in a humble fishing village. Fame and fortune had not been his lot; his influence had been held close to home. His greatest honor far outshone all the King's gold, for Lyte understood he was intimately known by God. And the rust and dust of life could never intrude upon this most precious treasure. Once inspired by the Emmaus bound disciples' plea, "Abide with us" (Luke 24:29, NKJV), this terminally ill country preacher lay on his death bed and penned the words of this petition that would carry him to the place "where moth and rust do not destroy" (Matt. 6:20).

Abide With Me

Abide with me; fast falls the eventide;
The darkness deepens; Lord, with me abide!
When other helpers fail and comforts flee,
Help of the helpless, O abide with me.

Swift to its close ebbs out life's little day;
Earth's joys grow dim; its glories pass away;
Change and decay in all around I see;
O Thou who changest not, abide with me.

I need Thy presence every passing hour;
What but Thy grace can foil the tempter's power?
Who, like Thyself, my guide and stay can be?
Through cloud and sunshine, Lord, abide with me.

I fear no foe, with Thee at hand to bless;
Ills have no weight, and tears no bitterness,
Where is death's sting? Where, grave, the victory?
I triumph still, if Thou abide with me.

Hold Thou Thy cross before my closing eyes;
Shine through the gloom and point me to the skies;
Heaven's morning breaks, and earth's vain shadows flee;
In life, in death, O Lord, abide with me.

Touch Stones

"O Lord, you have searched me and you know me.
You know when I sit and when I rise;
    you perceive my thoughts from afar.
You discern my going out and my lying down;
    you are familiar with all my ways."
Psalm 139:1-3

"Your Maker is your husband,
The Lord of hosts is His name;
and your Redeemer is the Holy One of Israel;
He is called the God of the whole earth."
Isaiah 54:5, NKJV

DAY ❊ ONE

Earthly Longings

Let me take you to the basement hallway that hosts our family photo gallery where I was once reminded of what real thirst looks like. My friend Joey had spent an afternoon at our home. Our four-year-old son, Connor, and I were walking with Joey when she began to notice the photos lining the wall.

She first noticed our oldest son's photos. "He's grown so much!" she exclaimed. "He was such a cute baby!" While she went on for a bit about Clayton's pictures, little brother Connor began to pat her on the leg. At first, this went unnoticed. So he patted faster and harder. When she finally looked down at Connor, he was pointing up to his own baby pictures. "Look!" he said. "That's me! I am Connor!"

Joey instinctively knelt down. "I know that you are Connor," she said, and she talked to him about his photos. My little Connor was deeply thirsty! Not for a juice box or a much-coveted root beer. Connor patted from a thirst that has existed from the dawn of time in the arid souls of all humanity. It's the thirst, the need, to be truly known.

King Solomon called the thirst of his soul *meaninglessness*. Saint Augustine described it as *restlessness*. The French philosopher and scientist, Pascal, depicted our deepest yearnings as a God-shaped vacuum, a void that insists on being filled.

To us, this thirst might show up as searching, a feeling of emptiness, or even discontent. Whatever you might call the dissatisfaction of soul you sometimes feel, this thirst reflects our need for a personal knowing touch from God. We crave God's intimate touch.

Consider some of the thirsty souls found in Scripture. Keep in mind that the people in the Bible represent you and me. We can see ourselves in their stories.

Look up the following passages. Record for each of the "parched people" what they thirsted for and what they received instead.

Scripture Passage	These Parched People	Thought they were thirsty for:	But this is the drink they received:
Gen. 3:1-6	Adam and Eve	Gen. 3:4-5	Gen. 3:22-23
Gen. 37:1-11	Joseph's brothers	Gen. 37:4, 8, 11	Gen. 41:57; 42:5-6
Josh. 6:1-19;7:1-2	Achan	Josh. 7:20-21	Josh. 7:25
Matt. 15:1-11	Pharisees	Matt. 15:6,9	Matt. 12:34-37;23:27-28

Adam and Eve thirsted for knowledge and received a cup of bitter awareness and spiritual death. Joseph's brothers thirsted for recognition but drank from the chalice of jealousy and submission. Achan tried to quench his thirst for material significance with stolen goods but discovered the goblet was filled with poison grapes. In Jesus' day, we read of the devoutly religious Pharisees who rejected the Living Water in exchange for a sip of putrid piety.

All these longings, searches, and thirsts picture the human spirit patting and pointing toward an unseen God. It's our sophisticated way of screaming, "I'm thirsty! Can't someone satisfy this deep longing? Here I am! Know me!"

I'm no different than the misguided thirsty souls in the table above and neither are you. For years I tried to satisfy my deep eternal longings by dipping my leaky water jug into shallow wells. Soap operas, romance novels, and shopping were all attempts at filling my longing for intimacy. I was trying to quench an intense, heavenly thirst with a few drops of tepid water. It didn't work then, and it doesn't work now.

Lots of us are so thirsty to be known that we dip into the rushing water of temporary satisfaction. Shallow relationships, low standards, promiscuity, compromise, and even outlandish behavior can all be buckets we dip into shallow water just to alleviate the intense craving even for a moment. Those drinks are from a bitter cup—and only leave us more desperately thirsty. Let's reflect for a moment on what we are thirsty for.

How do you seek to satisfy your longings?

❑ Perfect performance   ❑ denying the pain
❑ sacrificial service   ❑ attention-getting behavior
❑ compromising my values ❑ hiding
❑ people pleasing   ❑ other _____

What do you think you are really thirsty for?

_____

What kind of thirst does David describe in Psalm 42:1-2?

_____

David recognized that the small and momentary thirsts are quenched when our ultimate thirst is fully satisfied. Jesus, the Living Water, is the ultimate satisfaction.

Read what Jesus said in John 4:13-14.

Ask God to satisfy you with His Living Water. Complete the following prayer with your own words.

Oh God, You are the fountain of life. I know that I have been thirsty for …

_____

_____

I recognize that these thirsts can only be quenched by …

_____

_____

God, You have promised me that " 'If anyone is thirsty, let him come … and drink. Whoever believes … streams of living water will flow from within him' " (John 7:37-38). I believe that You know me, and because I know You, my thirst can be quenched. Please satisfy me with Your Living Water. Amen.

DAY ✿ TWO

Divine Visitation

As you read the following story, underline the words that describe the unfulfilled longings of my friend Yolanda's heart.

Yolanda was tired of the routine of life, wearied by rejection and emptied by harsh realities. Her family had rejected her. They even removed her pictures from the living room walls. She was dead in her mother's eyes. Her pain seemed stronger than her faith, so on Friday night she planned to take a bottle of sleeping pills.

Her friends, however, began to pester her to go to a prison on Friday with the campus ministry group. She continually refused, but they finally wore her down, and so she went. "After all," she thought, "I can take the pills when I get back."

During the prison service, she felt completely unmoved. Cold as stone.

Near the end of the meeting, an older man in a blue denim work shirt approached her. "Miss," he said, "I have a word for you from Isaiah 49:15." Yolanda quickly turned to the passage and read, "Can a mother forget the baby at her breast and have no compassion on the child she has borne? Though she may forget, I will not forget you!"

How could he have known?

How could a stranger know about her mother? About the rejection and emptiness? The incessant search for identity and purpose? How could he have known about the cleverly shrouded ache of her thirsty soul?

As Yolanda burst into tears, she looked up to thank the stranger. No one was there. No one in the locked and secured room fit the description of the man who had just visited her. With growing certainty—and awe—Yolanda realized she had been visited by One who was not a stranger. He was intimately acquainted with her. He knew all about her heartache and her secret thoughts. He visited her and touched her through His Word. And His touch, though not skin on skin, was more intimate and personal than any human touch could ever be.

Yolanda's plans changed in an instant because she felt the tender touch of God who came to her when she needed Him most. She knows how His touch filled her every longing to be accepted and whole. She is a reflection of the touch of a Father who knows us intimately. Maybe you've not been touched by God in such a dramatic fashion, but you can be sure that our Father who knows those who are His is not watching us from a distance. Rather, He is close. Close enough to touch you. Close enough to know you.

God used extraordinary means to make Himself known to Yolanda. He used a tailor-made provision to show her that He knew her.

In what extraordinary ways did God show up in the following ordinary lives?

Moses: Exodus 3:1-2 _____

Balaam: Numbers 22:21-33 _____

Isaiah: Isaiah 6:1-5 _____

Ezekiel: Ezekiel 37:1-10 _____

I'm sure you noticed God did something unique for each of these men. He obviously proficiently communicated through a burning bush, so why didn't He just use another burning bush to capture Balaam's attention? Or why didn't he send a talking donkey to meet Ezekiel? And why didn't He reveal Himself to Moses through a grand vision?

Ezekiel may have walked right past a burning bush, and Moses may have turned a deaf ear to a talking donkey! God reveals Himself to each of us individually. Because He knows us, He knows exactly how to get our attention. Now let's see how God got the attention of an ordinary woman at an ordinary well.

Read John 4:3-10.

For what did Jesus ask the woman (v. 7)? _____

What was her response? (v. 9) _____

The woman's harsh, hardened response to Jesus' simple request reveals that it wasn't just a well that stood between them—it was a wall. She obviously did not recognize Him, probably because she was distracted by what separated them.

The first distraction was gender. Ancient Hebrew culture didn't exactly highly favor women. In fact, they weren't favored at all. It was common to hear a Hebrew man praying with great relief and sincerity, "Lord, I thank You that I am not a woman." Rabbis proclaimed, "It is better to burn the law than to give it to a woman." That Jesus chose to engage a woman in conversation was only the first crack in the wall that divided them.

The second distraction was nationality. This woman wasn't just a foreigner, she was (of all things!) a Samaritan. Samaritans were despised as worthless half-breeds and spiritually-hollow opportunists. No orthodox Jew could stomach even setting foot on Samaritan turf. Rather than travel the easy route from Judea to Galilee, which goes through Samaria, the prejudiced Jews would add an extra few days to their journey by taking the desert route instead. When Jesus deliberately crossed the border into Samaria, He also crossed the barrier of hate—further chipping away at the wall of separation.

The third distraction was status. Jesus was a rabbi. Rabbis were highly regarded and lived by a strict code of conduct. They were not permitted to speak publicly to any woman— not even their wives or sisters. But Jesus was hardly just a teacher of law. He was both the giver and the fulfillment of the law. At the well He taught that His authority was greater than that of the law. And with this final blow, the wall of separation came tumbling down. The Samaritan woman had no idea with whom she spoke. And she had no idea how close she was to the intimate touch of God.

God seeks you right in the middle of your everyday life just like He sought Yolanda, Moses, Balaam, and the woman at the well. He seeks you in the midst of the millions just so He can reveal Himself to you. Do you see Him in the crowd, or do you miss Him because you are distracted by your own plans?

What distractions does Satan use to keep you from clearly seeing God's work in your life?

_____

_____

Sometimes our plans and longings get in the way and they only serve to blur our view, keeping us from recognizing God's presence in our most ordinary moments.

Remember what the woman at the well held in her hands? Her water jug. Her jug kept her focus on her plans, her task to be accomplished. It kept her from recognizing Jesus.

Consider. What plans do you have that keep you so distracted that you fail to notice your divine visitation?

_____

Sometimes we expect to meet God only in a sanctuary or worship center and not in our ordinary plans. The Samaritan woman met Jesus and felt His touch at the village well. In the midst of her daily routine, God stepped in and made her ordinary extraordinary. God seeks to do the same for you and me. In the course of our everyday lives, God steps in, intrigues us, exposes our need, and reveals Himself to us. Why? Because God knows us and wants us to know Him.

Ask God to reveal Himself to you over the next three days as He touches you in the ordinary routine of life. Keep a record in your journal of the ways He touches you. God may not show up at your well (or your dishwasher) in the same way He appeared in Samaria. He often uses a "still, small voice" (1 Kings 19:12, NKJV). Keep your eyes and heart open.

DAY ❀ THREE

Full and Running Over

We've been talking about God knowing us and wanting us to know Him. Let's look into how He knows us and how we can know Him more.

Look up *know* in a dictionary or thesaurus. Record below definitions or synonyms to complete the phrases. Read each phrase aloud, and thank God that He knows you!

God _____ me.   God _____ me.

God _____ me.   God _____ me.

God _____ me.

God repeatedly says in His Word that He knows you. Let's see what He says.

Connect the reference at the left with its matching Scripture phrase on the right.

Isaiah 49:16   He knows those who are His.
John 1:48   He has engraved your image on the palms of His hands.
John 10:3   He knows your name.
1 Corinthians 8:3   You are known by God.
2 Timothy 2:19   God sees and recognizes you.

Choose one of these verses to write on a note card and memorize. On the back of the card, paraphrase and personalize the verse in your own words.

Knowing God and being known by Him bring us the ultimate satisfaction in life. Only heavenly things can satisfy our thirst, for we are not of this world. Before God created the world, He had a unique plan for each of us. Because He knows us intimately, He can craft a plan that quenches our deepest thirsts.

Jesus often exposes our need before he satisfies it. Let's return to the Samaritan well to see what Jesus said that exposed the woman's need.

What was the woman's response in John 4:17?

_____

What if she had responded, "Uh, he's not home," or "I can't leave the well." "My cell phone battery is awfully low!" What if she had made excuses to cover up her thirst?

Do you make excuses? Do you cover up, veil your empty, ugly places from Jesus? He will reveal Himself to you when you are honest with Him—when you are willing to listen, to inquire, and to linger at the well.

Jesus spoke startling words to the woman in response to her inquiries about the Messiah. Look at what Jesus said in John 4:26, "I who speak to you am He" (NKJV).

Think of it! At this point, Jesus had not yet revealed Himself—even to His closest followers—with such a definitive, authoritative statement. I think that in the kind heart of God, He had reserved an intimate revelation for this woman. A sexually loose Samaritan woman. Amazing! As if to say, "There is no one whom I deem unworthy of My intimate touch. I want to know you. You, who are stained and ordinary. I want to meet you at your well and satisfy you. I want you to know Me, too. I will reveal Myself to you in truth and intimacy if you just linger at the well long enough to listen and inquire of Me."

> "Jesus declared,
>
> 'I who speak to
>
> you am he.' "
>
> **John 4:26**

The first and last words of this phrase from John 4:26 identify who Jesus is. Write these two words in the first and last blanks:

"_____ ... _____ _____."

Now, fill in the remaining blank that completes Jesus' thought.

When Jesus revealed Himself to the woman in Sychar, He basically said, "I AM." Jesus used the words, "I AM" when describing Himself to His followers and curious onlookers, and He uses the same to reveal Himself to us.

Record from John 8:58 how Jesus describes Himself: _____ _____

Read John 18:3-8. Notice how Jesus refers to Himself in this passage. Twice He says, "I AM." What was the response of the chief priests, Pharisees, and soldiers to Jesus' pronouncement in verse 6?

_____

Why do you think those words caused such a reaction?

_____

The first time God told Moses His name, He said, " 'I AM WHO I AM' " (Ex. 3:14). The Hebrew word *hayah* means "I AM." So when Jesus referred to Himself by the name I AM, He was using

God's name. For Jesus to call Himself, "I AM," was to call Himself God. No wonder He made the religious establishment so angry—He claimed to be God!

Scripture records more than 60 "I AM" statements. For example, " 'I AM WHO I AM' " (Ex. 3:14); " 'I am a Father to Israel' " (Jer. 31:9, KJV); " 'I am the Alpha and the Omega' " (Rev. 1:8); " 'I am for you (Rom. 8:31, KJV); " 'I am from above' " (John 8:23); " 'I am He that liveth' " (Rev. 1:18, KJV); " 'I am he who searches hearts' " (Rev. 2:23); " 'I am meek and lowly' " (Matt. 11:29, KJV); " 'I am the bread of life' " (John 6:35); " 'I am the Lord, who heals you' " (Ex. 15:26); " 'I am the Root' " (Rev. 22:16); " 'I am your exceeding and great reward' " (Gen. 15:1, KJV).

When we fix our spiritual eyes on the face of Jesus, we begin to recognize that whatever our thirst, He satisfies through His presence, through His "I AM."

When you hunger for acceptance or crave a sense of satisfaction, what does Jesus reveal about Himself to you (John 6:35,51)?

_____

When you are confused and things don't make sense, or you feel hopeless or sad, what does Jesus tell you He can be in your darkness (John 8:12; 9:5)?

_____

When you feel as if you're unprotected or insecure, what do the I AM statements in John 10:7,9 mean to you?

_____

When you need guidance and comfort, what does Jesus tell you He is (John 10:11,14)?

_____

When all seems lost, when a terminal disease is diagnosed, when a loved one dies, what does Jesus reveal at the well of heartache (John 11:25)?

_____

When you are concerned that you are being deceived, lied to, or misguided, what does Jesus say (John 14:6)?

_____

When you feel powerless or disconnected, what does Jesus say to you (John 15:1,5)?

_____

When you need a strong foundation, a sense of comfort, what I AM will satisfy this thirst (Rev. 1:8,17)?

_____

_____

Which of the "I AM" statements from pages 30-32 meet your deepest longings or quench your thirst today? Write this I AM verse on a note card and meditate on it this week. Rephrase this or another I AM statement as a YOU ARE prayer. For example, _Lord, I thank You that_ YOU ARE ... Write your prayer in your journal.

We can receive no more intimate touch than to hear Jesus reveal Himself. His invitation is clear. "I am the Alpha and the Omega, the Beginning and the End. To him who is thirsty I will give to drink without cost from the spring of the water of life" (Rev. 21:6).

DAY ❀ FOUR

Welcome Him to Your Well

If you're like me, you're not studying your Bible in a serene study surrounded by candles. No, you're probably in a worn-out recliner or at a kitchen table surrounded by yesterday's paper, a stack of bills, and a half full (or half empty) coffee cup! I hope that by this time in the study you're starting to recognize God's visitation in your ordinary moments.

What happened when the woman at the well recognized Jesus' divine visitation (John 4:28-30).

You see, the woman's plans utterly changed (John 4:28-29). She left a meaningless, empty water jug by the well because she had tasted living water for the first time. She had been invited to know the God who knew her—and she went to invite others to know Him, too. Look back at the cover-up responses at the top of page 30 and consider what buckets you carry. Just because your bucket isn't listed there, don't think you're off the hook! Carefully consider what you use to try to fill yourself up, to satisfy your thirst. Remember that Living Water awaits those who are willing to leave those water jugs behind!

Do you need to discover whether you have some empty jugs you need to leave at the well so you can be filled by Jesus alone? Circle the number that most closely matches your response to the following statements.

	Never	Rarely	Sometimes	Often	Always
I feel others really don't understand me.	1	2	3	4	5
I feel disconnected from God.	1	2	3	4	5
I feel empty.	1	2	3	4	5
I struggle with discontent.	1	2	3	4	5
I'm dissatisfied.	1	2	3	4	5

If you got mostly 4s and 5s, head to the closest Jugs 'R Us because "there's a hole in your bucket, dear Liza", and the living water is leaking out. If you got mostly 2s and 3s, dip your jug a little deeper because living water is rarely found at the surface of life. If you got mostly 1s and 2s, you're brimming with living water, but remember that you're still a jar of clay (and you need to finish this Bible study)!

Regardless of what you scored on this little quiz, Jesus is waiting to be welcomed to your well. In fact, when you recognize Him there, you'll find Him ready to satisfy your thirst completely. Let's see how Jesus can satisfy and fill us to the brim.

Let's consider what Jesus came to do by filling in the blanks below.

_____ you with His love as He rejoices over you with singing (Zeph. 3:17).

_____ you with gracious words from His lips (Luke 4:22).

_____ you near when you were far away (Eph. 2:13).

_____ you to springs of living water (Rev. 7:17).

Look at the journal you began on day 2. Compare your entries with the verbs you wrote in the blanks above, and then answer the following: What has God done to …

lead you? _____

amaze you? _____

quiet you? _____

bring you near?_____

I hope you've recognized the times over the last few days when God has quieted you with His love. I hope you have truly been brought near to Him and been amazed as He leads you in paths of righteousness.

God may not use burning bushes, talking donkeys, or walking sets of bones to tell you He knows you. But it will be clear. "It will be "exceedingly abundantly above all that we ask or think" (Eph. 3:20, NKJV).

Don't let your buckets keep you from experiencing the fullness of God's touch. Leave them at the well and be filled by Him. Then, my friend, when you get jostled, what spills out will be life-giving, life-sustaining water.

Close your study today with a time of prayer. Review with Jesus what you've been studying about Him this week.

DAY ❀ FIVE
Soul Satisfaction

Christmas 2002 was the first major holiday we celebrated with my new assistant, Katie. She had only been on board a few months when the artificial evergreen went up in my living room. She and I had worked together, traveled, written e-mails, edited newsletters, and done a million other odd tasks. So, when it came time for the ministry gift exchange, I handed her a fluffy gift bag, and she did the same for me. We pulled out the tissue and found gift certificates to restaurants and candle shops!

Well, Katie has been with us almost two years now. This past Christmas, after a year of intense work together which included being stranded in airports, filming a video series, keeping up with a weird and unpredictable schedule, Katie and I once again presented each other with Christmas gift bags.

Now, I will admit I suffer from a malady called "gift anxiety." I'm never sure what to buy or how much to spend. I'm forever second-guessing myself, "Will she like this?" or "What if it doesn't fit?" But, even so, I shopped and came up with the perfect gift for Katie.

As she pulled out the tissue, she giggled at the travel shampoo and mousse I included and thanked me for the lotion she liked, but then she gasped! "I can't believe you got me licorice!" Yes, an $.89 bag of black licorice was the highlight of the gift bag! You see, Katie had said in passing once that she loved licorice. By some miracle of cognitive processing, I remembered! Even I could see how much the simple bag of licorice meant to her, and I was thrilled! The licorice was the most meaningful gift because it confirmed that I really knew her, noticed her, listened to her, and cared!

After only a few months of her being on the job, I knew about her—but one Christmas later, I knew her! It means a lot to us to know that someone really knows us—not just knows about us, but actually knows our flaws, our tastes, our insecurities, and our strengths. God knows us that intimately, and He's still captivated by us. He hears what you say and knows what you love. By some miracle of divine creativity, He'll show you that you are on His mind.

Why did God use a burning bush with Moses, a donkey with Balaam, a stranger with Yolanda, and Himself as a weary Jewish traveler at a well? The same reason I stuck licorice in a gift bag—it's a personal touch. It's a way to communicate, "I know you!" God seeks to reveal Himself to you in a unique and personal way. Why? Because you are unique and He tailor makes His touch to be personal. He might not use licorice or a burning bush with you, but I guarantee He'll reveal Himself in a way that you will recognize if you simply open your eyes of faith. He comes in many different ways, but He comes with one purpose. He comes to show you that He alone is the ultimate satisfaction. But don't miss this point! Being satisfied by the blessings of God is different than being satisfied by God Himself. In fact, being satisfied by blessings alone can actually leave you feeling isolated and alone.

Read:	How did God satisfy the children of Israel?	What did He caution them about?
Deut. 6:10-19		
Deut. 8:6-14		
Deut. 11:14-16		

Now read Hosea 13:6 to see how the children of Israel threw caution to the wind and were caught up in the cyclone of isolation from God.

Having our needs met and being ultimately satisfied are two different things. Satisfying our needs is not the same as satisfying our souls. We can easily believe that just because our earthly longings are satisfied our heavenly thirst is quenched. However, we will still be thirsty until we have the ultimate satisfaction of intimacy with God Himself. That only comes through His Word.

In the following passages God tells the children of Israel and us what to do to be satisfied. In your own words, what is God telling you to do so that He can satisfy you?

Deuteronomy 11:18-20 _____

_____

Jeremiah 15:16 _____

_____

Matthew 4:4 _____

_____

Separation from God and His Word alienates us from the one thing for which we long. The psalmist understood this. In Psalm 119:9, David compares himself to a stranger when he is distant or separated from God's Word.

Circle the word that best describes how you feel when you are separated from God's Word.

Lonely	Aimless	Guilty	Disenfranchised	Wanting	Empty
Outsider	Insecure	Doubtful	Disconnected	other:_____	

We are strangers until God's Word satisfies us with intimacy. You see, knowing God through His Word allows us to feel the satisfaction of being known. The great Apostle Paul knew this too. Check out this phrase from his letter to the Galatians: "now that you know God—or rather are known by God" (Gal. 4:9). You see, knowing God is inextricably linked to being known by Him. When you recognize Him in your life, you begin to truly know Him. Then you will see that He can fully meet your need to be known. Only that personal connection with God brings us lasting satisfaction.

God's touch is personal. How can you share the touch you've received?

Touch Point
Everybody has a button he or she needs to have pushed. You know what I mean. When Katie pulled licorice out of a gift bag, I knew I had pushed her button marked, "You really know me!" Some button bearers in your life really need to feel God's touch. So turn on your button radar and take notice of what really communicates that you know them and God does too. Chocolate? Vacuuming? Babysitting? Encouragement? Whatever it is, do or say something for someone this week that will remind them that you know something special about them. And as you do, remember that you are extending God's personal and knowing touch.

---

[1]"Lexicon Results for *hayah* (Strong's 01961)," *Blue Letter Bible* [online], [cited 20 October, 2004]. Available from the Internet: *www.blueletterbible.org*.

Listening Guide

God places within us the _____ to be _____;

Only _____ can fulfill our longing to be known.

Oftentimes in relationships we substitute _____ for _____.

You will never recognize _____ really knows you until _____ know God.

God seeks to _____ Himself to us in our _____ moments.

When we seek Him, _____ is the one who _____ being found.

At your well of _____, the Lord your God is with you.

His Redeeming Touch

Charles and John Wesley pondered for hours as they galloped beyond the church walls preaching the truth of Jesus' love! They traveled the English countryside to bring God's redeeming touch to illiterate miners and destitute farmers who would never enter a cathedral. They touched with God's love those who lived on society's margins—the tattered and torn God could touch with redemption.

Charles knew God's touch that had redeemed him would redeem anyone who would just receive. As his steed clip-clopped from one village to another, he considered God's amazing love for hours. I'm glad he did, for those hours yielded the words to a favorite hymn. As you read these words, feel the touch of God who pursues us and desires to call us His very own.

And Can It Be?

And can it be that I should gain
An interest in the Saviour's blood?
Died He for me, who caused His
    pain?
For me, who Him to death
pursued?

Amazing love! how can it be
That Thou, my Lord, shouldst die
    for me?

He left His Father's throne above,
So free, so infinite His grace!
Emptied Himself of all but love,
And bled for Adam's helpless race!
'Tis mercy all, immense and free,
For, O my God, it found out me.

'Tis mystery all! Th' Immortal dies!
Who can explore His strange design?
In vain the first born seraph tries

To sound the depths of love divine.
'Tis mercy all! let earth adore;
Let angel minds inquire no more.

Long my imprisoned spirit lay
Fast bound in sin and nature's night.
Thine eye diffused a quickening ray;
I woke—the dungeon flamed with
    light!
My chains fell off, my heart was free,
I rose, went forth, and followed Thee.

No condemnation now I dread;
Jesus, and all in Him is mine;
Alive in Him, my living Head,
And clothed in righteousness
    divine,
Bold I approach the'eternal throne,
And claim the crown, through
    Christ my own.

Touch Stones

"Praise the Lord, O my soul,
    and forget not all his benefits—
who forgives all your sins
    and heals all your diseases,
who redeems your life from the pit
    and crowns you with love and compassion,
who satisfies your desires with good things
    so that your youth is renewed like the eagle's."
Psalm 103:2-5

"In Him we have redemption through His blood,
the forgiveness of sins, according to the riches
of His grace." Ephesians 1:7, NKJV

DAY ❀ ONE

Gotcha Day

As we wheeled our luggage out the door, Cinda (a new friend from the women's conference in Kentucky) announced, "I need to hurry home. Today is Gotcha Day!"

Gotcha Day? I mused. *What in the world is Gotcha Day?* I raced through my mental calendar, and no such holiday emerged. Maybe I hadn't heard her right. Maybe her parents were Jewish, and she had actually said, "It's Matzo Day!" Or perhaps "Gotcha Day" was German for Saturday … or something. Finally, I couldn't stand it any longer. "All right, you knew I was going to ask! Now what in the world is 'Gotcha Day'?"

Cinda giggled. She reminded me that her two precious children were adopted. Gotcha Day is a huge and joyful celebration commemorating the day the children joined their family. In their household, Gotcha Day is as big as a birthday. Maybe bigger. What a marvelous reason to have a party!

My Gotcha Day was March 25, 1973. I know specifically when it was, because I chose to be "gotten." No, I wasn't adopted into my earthly family (my mom has hospital bills to prove otherwise!). I was adopted into the family of God when I was only nine years old. I remember it vividly and even wrote down the time it occurred on the page separating the Old and New Testaments in my first Bible.

It was 8:35 p.m. That's the very moment I felt God's redeeming touch on me as He gently pulled me close to His heart and made me His very own.

The "Before" Picture

To more deeply experience the amazing transformation of God's redeeming touch, remember life before He touched you.

Before God "got" me …

Describe in the margin your life before God "got" you.

If you came to Christ as a child, becoming a Christian may not have made a noticeable difference in your life … you simply continued being "nice." It seems to me that God's children come in two varieties. Some of us know what we've been saved from because we lived that unredeemed life; others of us know what we've been saved from only because we're willing to accept what Scripture says about our desperate plight without Christ.

Let's spend some time in God's Word reminding ourselves of the life we've been "gotten" from … whether or not we've lived out the earthly results.

Look at Romans 8:6-8, and describe the mind of a sinful person: _____

_____

Prayerfully circle any portion of your description that is true now. Don't skip this.

Between what two things did the Galatian Christians struggle (Gal. 2:21–3:5)?

_____ and _____

The Galatian Christians were much like us. We know our good behavior doesn't earn God's favor, but sometimes we think we've at least earned points with God. This kind of thinking keeps God at a distance. When we live by a law of our own making, we proclaim a hidden belief that, as nice as He is, we really don't need God. Rather than relying on our own effort, we must each courageously place our life alongside the biblical standard of believing God.

Pause to pray; ask God whether you, even as a Christian, have held Him at a distance, relying on your goodness to be good enough. Journal your thoughts.

What five words or phrases from Ephesians 2:1-3 describe our lives as they used to be?

1. _____   4. _____

2. _____   5. _____

3. _____

What motivated God to offer us an escape from those things (vv. 4-5)?

The "After" Picture

We were once orphans needing to be "gotten," and God chose us. He made us members of His family, calling us His children. Hear and believe Jesus' words: " 'You did not choose Me but I chose you' " (John 15:16, HCSB). These words ought to shatter our foolish pride and self-righteousness forever.

Adoption is the perfect picture of being chosen. In the first-century Roman world an adopted son was chosen to carry the adoptive family's name and inherit that family's estate. Once completed, the adoption was absolute. The person who had been adopted enjoyed all the privileges of a legitimate son in his new family.

From Ephesians 1:3-14 list 10 words or phrases that describe our lives now:

1. _____   6. _____

2. _____   7. _____

3. _____   8. _____

4. _____   9. _____

5. _____   10. _____

Circle the one from your list that is most precious to you. Take time to journal your thoughts and explain your choice.

Read Romans 8:15-17. The phrase translated "Spirit of sonship" (NIV) is also translated "Spirit of adoption" (HCSB). Describe life as God's adopted child:

_____

Of all the incredible blessings you've just listed, crying out to God as "Abba" may be the sweetest of all. Jesus used the same word when He cried out to God from the garden of Gethsemane (see Mark 14:36). This convinces me that we as adopted children enjoy all the privileges of the only begotten Son in the household—Jesus Himself.

Write a prayer in your journal. Address God as "Abba" and thank Him for adopting you. Then, read your prayer and record any lingering thoughts or emotions.

According to Galatians 4: 4-7, how do we become God's heir?

_____

_____

In the familiar story in Mark 10:17-22, the rich young man trusted the law; he was counting on obeying the law to matter to God. And what did he ask? "Good teacher, … what must I do to inherit eternal life?" (v. 17). He wanted more to do, more rules to follow, more checklists of right and wrong—all things that he could control and manage, and all designed so he could know when the work of securing his salvation was complete.

Jesus didn't ask the young man to do more for his salvation; Jesus called him to follow. Jesus offered him the inheritance God gives to His children, but at these offers, the young "man's face fell. He went away sad" (v. 22). This disciplined, biblically literate man was eager to be good but not willing to risk being God's.

What about you? Have you ever been content to be good so you could shield yourself from being God's? Describe that choice and its outcome in your journal.

Ephesians 3:14-21 is a beautiful prayer with a wonderful perspective on who we are and what we've inherited as God's adopted children. Rewrite these verses in your journal. Expressing gratitude for all you've inherited because God has chosen you.

Perhaps you noticed these verses are Paul's prayer for the Ephesian Christians, not a prayer for or about himself. Continue your prayer time, using this passage to intercede for a dear friend, for your Bible study group, or for your church.

We once were under the authority of sin and despair; but since our adoption, we now thrive under the protective shade of our new family tree! We are "dearly loved children" (Eph. 5:1) and "children of light" (5:8). We have been given "the right to become children of God … born of God" (John 1:12-13). Yes, we've been gotten!

DAY ❀ TWO
Orphan No More

Growing up, I often heard a line in commercials—"this product has the Good Housekeeping Seal of Approval." I remember thinking, *That's the one I want!* Have you ever opened a package for a new appliance, toy, or even a package of socks and seen the slip of paper, Inspected by #3? As silly as it may sound, when I see those tags, I feel as if someone is looking out for me!

When God chose you to be in His family, He placed His seal on you. Far better than a seal that assures a product is good, God's seal of ownership assures you are God's own.

Begin your journal entries today by writing 2 Corinthians 1:21-22. Substitute your name for the pronouns to personalize its message.

In ancient cultures, a seal showed ownership. Seals made of wax, moist clay, or ink served to authenticate covenants, contracts, decrees, and other legal documents. The ancient seal was used as our signature is today: it identified the owner, represented a promise, and guaranteed authenticity.

On our adoption day, we too were sealed. Can you feel the warm wax? Can you sense the gentle pressure of God's signet ring sealing you as His own for all of time and eternity? He signed His name on your heart and marked you as His own.

Sketch in the margin what you imagine God's seal of ownership looks like on you.

Where is God's seal placed on you? Is it ❑ easily detected or ❑ somewhat hidden?

Paul repeated this image to the Ephesians, "You also were included in Christ when you heard the word of truth, the gospel of your salvation. Having believed, you were marked in him with a seal, the promised Holy Spirit" (Eph. 1:13).

Compare Ephesians 1:13 with 2 Corinthians 1:21-22. What is our evidence that God's seal is present in our lives?

_____

The Holy Spirit is God's seal, His mark of ownership. The promised Holy Spirit is the very fingerprint of God, always leaving His impression on our lives.

Jesus told His disciples about the Holy Spirit during His last hours with them. His words reassured and comforted them. He wanted them to know they would be cared for and guided. Through the Holy Spirit, they were as close to Him as they had been during His physical life.

Review the following verses from those last hours Jesus spent with His disciples. Beside each reference, write the Holy Spirit's activity or mission:

John 14:16 _____

John 14:17 _____

John 14:26 _____

John 15:26 _____

John 16:8-11 _____

John 16:13 _____

John 16:14-15 _____

Review your list above, and mark your answers with the following symbols:
! "This was new to me; I'd never seen it before today!"
? "I'm not sure I understand this part of the Holy Spirit's work in me."
* "This is most meaningful to me today."
# "I've ignored this work of the Spirit in my life."
✓ "I need this to help me with _____."
                                    (some difficulty you are facing)

When we experience these promises, we feel the invisible touch of God, and it forever changes us! To seal us as His children, God sent the Spirit of His Son into our hearts, the Spirit who cries out, "Father, my Father" (Gal. 4:6, TEV).

Pray about issues stirred in your mind and heart through your study. Journal things to remember and review. Invite the Holy Spirit to make His mark evident in your life.

God has chosen us! He has sealed us, and we bear His name. Daniel put it this way when he prayed, "Your people bear your Name" (Dan. 9:19).

Begin singing to yourself the first verse of the hymn "Amazing Grace" (it's OK ... no one is listening!) What does it say you once were? And now are?

Use the following Scriptures to help you label the following lines:

"I once was ..."   **"But now I'm ..."**
_____lost_____   _____found_____

Luke 15:19-24

_____   _____

John 15:15

_____   _____

Romans 9:25-26

_____   _____

Ephesians 2:13

_____   _____

Ephesians 2:19

_____   _____

Ephesians 5:8

_____   _____

1 Peter 2:10

_____   _____

Mark each line to indicate where you are in Christ. For example, is your life more representative of being lost or being found? Journal your thoughts about this exercise.

We are now and forever children of the heavenly Father, and "neither death nor life, neither angels nor demons, neither the present nor the future, nor any powers, neither height nor depth, nor anything else in all creation, will be able to separate us from the love of God that is in Christ Jesus our Lord" (Rom. 8:38-39).

Since I first felt His redeeming touch, I've deeply loved *Abba* and every word He speaks. I marvel at this; I'm captivated by His compassion. I often weep in church as we sing, "Thank You for the cross, My Friend." That cross and Jesus' willingness to die on it made my adoption possible—I walked into God's throne room through its costly doorway.

Finish today with a fun and faith-enhancing assignment! With supplies from around your house, design an invitation for your own "Gotcha Day Party!" Portray this day's meaning through the design, colors, and images you use. Add "Who? What? When? Where? Why?" information needed on any invitation. Enjoy this! You'll display and explain this project at this week's group meeting.

DAY ❀ THREE

Because I Love You

Little Kirsten taught me a lesson about God's love and His redeeming touch. Just a few days shy of Kirsten's second birthday, her mother, Debbi, was taken to heaven. I can't imagine the difficult path Kirsten's father, Scott, walked as he guided his young daughter down this path of grief.

People from the church rallied to help. One of them was Marcey. She was in her late 20s—vivacious, bright, generous, and single. During the year that followed Debbi's death, Scott and Marcey forged a friendship. Their friendship became affection; their affection, love.

On August 26, 2000, Scott kissed Marcey for the first time as they stood together at the altar as bride and groom. Not long afterward, Marcey and three-year-old Kirsten were traveling in the car together. "Mommy," Kirsten said, "I used to call you Marcey, and now I call you Mommy. Why?" Marcey's mind raced with all the possible answers explaining Debbi's death. She finally summed it up by saying, "Because I love you."

That's what it truly means to be a daughter. We are loved. We were once distant from God; our sin alienated us from a relationship with Him. We knew of Him as Creator and Judge—great, high, and fearsome—but now through Jesus we know Him as Father. Just because He loves us.

Our striving and merit don't seat us in heavenly places with Him. We're elegible for that position simply because He loves us. Little Kirsten didn't have to earn Marcey's love. When Marcey said, "I do" to Scott, she also said "I do" to Kirsten, simply out of love. On the day you entered God's family, the Father said an unconditional "I do" to you, and the steadfast love of our Lord never changes.

Even though God's love never changes, sometimes our lives do. Relationships change, circumstances spin out of our control, and we find ourselves feeling alone. Maybe you've felt that way lately. You may have wondered if God was really present and if He was paying attention. My friend, He was there. His hand has always been on you. He is a good Father. He is a perfect Parent. Your Abba Father has promised, "Never will I leave you; never will I forsake you" (Heb. 13:5).

Parenting is no small task! Write a job description for the ideal parent:

_____

_____

_____

_____

If you memorized Bible verses as a child, likely the first was "God is love" (1 John 4:16). When Bible verses describe love, they describe God. So, find the familiar love chapter, 1 Corinthians 13. As you see the qualities of love it lists, look for that quality in your job description above. Circle it, and write the reference beside it.

Most likely you found many parallels between your job description of an ideal parent and the qualities of God's love. We naturally base our perception of God on our experiences with our earthly fathers. If your dad was harsh or disapproving, you might expect those same qualities in your heavenly Father. If your dad was absent, indifferent, passive, or cold— it might be difficult to believe that God is present, loving, and caring.

If, on the other hand, you grew up with a dad who was kind, attentive, and consistent, it's a little easier to step into a trusting relationship with your unseen heavenly Father. Not all of us have good memories of being someone's physical child; but through God's incredible love, each of us can know the experiences of nurturing, encouragement, discipline, forgiveness, and love that comes only from our heavenly Father.

Draw a line matching each passage below with its statement about God's love.

Genesis 1:27	I displayed My love when I sent My Son to die for you.
Psalm 139:1	My love for you will never end.
Jeremiah 31:3	I know everything about you.
John 17:23	You are my offspring … my family.
Acts 17:28	I made you in My image.
Romans 5:8; I John 4:9	You are My child!
Ephesians 1:11	I love you just as much as I love Jesus.
Ephesians 1:12	You are designed for the praise of My glory.
I John 3:1	I am love itself.
I John 4:16	I've chosen you to be mine.

When I had my physical sight, I can remember looking at someone I knew very well and then suddenly seeing him or her in a whole new way. Some aspect of physical appearance or personality caught my eye for the first time, and it was as though I were seeing that person with fresh eyes.

How long has it been since you've seen God with fresh eyes?

_____

What aspect of God caught your spiritual eye for the first time today, earlier this week, or maybe for the first time in a long time?

_____

With God we have much to see, know, and experience. His character has many aspects and His love many facets. Because He loves you, He calls you His own. He is a good Father, completely trustworthy and loving. He longs to lavish you with all the benefits of His glorious inheritance. He has touched your life, and that touch was redeeming. Can you sense His hand and His touch?

You are His daughter, chosen and dearly loved. Thank God for the privilege of calling Him Father. Use your journal to capture your thoughts and prayers. Consider memorizing one of the Scriptures you've studied today. Record it in your journal as well.

DAY ❋ FOUR

Brought Near

As my friend Christin and I watched our children play together, she said all she'd ever wanted was to be a wife and mother. She and her husband Lane had planned since their engagement for a house full of kids, but just months before their wedding, Christin's doctors discovered extensive tumors. Amidst bridal showers and wedding plans, she had major surgery. Five surgeries followed, including a complete hysterectomy at age 28.

Christin mourned the loss of her dream to bear children. She never wore maternity clothes, but she and Lane gladly donned traveling clothes when they learned that over 600,000 children in Russia needed homes. In June 1999, they received a video of a tiny baby boy, lying on his tummy and looking at the camera with eyes as big as quarters. "From the very first sight of that little boy," Christin said, "we knew he was ours. Nothing is harder than knowing your child is somewhere in the world alive, but you aren't with him." Six weeks later, the family of two journeyed to Russia where they became a family of three.

As they first held their precious son, they could barely see him because their eyes were full of tears! They were finally parents! The sentiments Christin and Lane felt must reflect the sentiments God feels for His orphaned children. He knew us and longed for us even when we were far away. His heart must ache knowing His child is alive in the world but not "alive in Christ" (see Eph. 2:4-5, *The Message*). We are all like baby Joshua, waiting to be "gotten"! Our Father God rescues us just as we are.

Now an energetic preschooler, Joshua loves to tell his baby story: "Once upon a time, there was a mommy and daddy who wanted a baby so bad, so they prayed that Jesus would give them a baby. God sent them a picture, and they got on a plane and flew all the way to 'Brussia,' and got their baby and held on tight. They flew all the way back and had a big party at the airport."

Our story is like Joshua's. Our Father loved us so much that He came and got us, and there was a big party in heaven when we came home. Paul wrote: "Remember that at that time you were separate from Christ … without hope and without God in the world. But now in Christ Jesus you who once were far away have been brought near through the blood of Christ" (Eph. 2:12-13).

Notice that before our adoption we were without God and without hope. Hope is essential for a whole, healthy life. Define hope if you were …

critically ill _____

financially strapped _____

mourning a loved one's death _____

searching for a job _____

Express your feelings about the promise of hope in Colossians 1:27:

_____

_____

_____

As you ponder what you've written in your definitions, don't miss this truth: Hope is not a wish or a daydream. Hope is Jesus Himself in you and me. It's not possible to be brought any nearer to God than that!

This hope is what His redeeming touch is all about! He reaches across an otherwise impossible chasm, grasps someone lost and far away, and brings her home. God, who desires to be our Father, went to unimaginable lengths to draw us to Himself. He allowed His own Son to bridge on a cross the great chasm separating us from Him. He came to us when we were abandoned, orphaned, and alone. He found us, small and needy, and made us His own. He embraced us and held us in His heart. "Long ago, even before he made the world, God loved us and chose us in Christ … His unchanging plan has always been to adopt us into his own family by bringing us to himself through Jesus Christ" (Eph. 1:4-5, NLT).

Jesus illustrated this awesome truth in Luke 15, the chapter of lost things. Read the first story in verses 3-7. The statements below are illustrated in this story. Write the biblical words or phrases that reveal God's eternal plan to adopt you:

1. God finds the one who's lost rather than the one who's lost finding God:

_____

2. God's response to finding a straying sheep is joy, not anger:

_____

By the way, what is the ratio of found sheep to lost sheep? ___ : ___

You were once that one lost sheep. Having 99 sheep safely secured seems to be immaterial to this story. You are so valuable to the Good Shepherd that He pursues you, scoops you up in His arms, and rejoices! You may not feel worthy of a party in your honor, but that's exactly what happens! For millennia the halls of heaven have resonated with great rejoicing each time an orphan has come home or a straying one has been found.

Now read the second short story of lostness in Luke 15:8-10. Would you rather be compared to a sheep or a coin? ❏ sheep ❏ coin

And what about the ratio of found to lost in this story? We've gone from a ratio of 99 to 1 in the previous story to a ratio of 9 to 1 in this one. Why do you think Jesus was so careful to capture the numbers of sheep and coins in this story?

_____

_____

We find one more story in Luke 15—perhaps the most beloved parable Jesus told. Settle in with your Bible and a cup of tea. Begin reading with verse 11, and savor this very familiar saga about a lost son as you read to the end of the chapter.

We can study and say much about this story. Answer in your journal two questions every prodigal must answer: How far away can you run from God? and How close do you get to God when you return?

Dear Christian, you too can be a prodigal, and no one knows it but you and your heavenly Father. In many ways you can turn your back on God or keep your distance from Him, even among those who are His own.

Pause to pray. Confess any attitudes, choices, or actions that have made you God's prodigal. What do you sense is God's reply to your confession?

_____

_____

As you ponder what you've just written and what you've just experienced in prayer, return to the Scripture once more. Read Genesis 41:39-43 and Esther 6:8,11 and 8:2,8. What two like items were given as gifts in these stories?

_____ and _____

What is the meaning behind those gifts?_____

_____

These gifts signified acceptance, and even more amazingly, the conferring of authority by the powerful. Notice the signet ring again, the seal that proves to whom we belong and to whom we bow.

When God's lost children are found, there is "rejoicing in heaven" (Luke 15:7). I'm sure the angels blow their trumpets and exclaim, "Hallelujah!" I can almost hear the saints that have gone before clapping, cheering, and praising. But I think one voice rings above the gleeful exaltation. One voice like joyful thunder. The voice of our Father God leads the "Welcome home!" chorus.

God loves you … God **loves** you … God loves **you!**

DAY ❀ FIVE

Beautiful in His Time

An interviewer recently asked, "If you could see just one thing for one moment, what would it be?" I paused and pondered the question. Then with confidence, I answered, "I'd reject the offer! To me, it would be like Lay's Potato Chips … you can't eat just one!"

The interviewer laughed, and I continued, "I'd hesitate to choose one thing because I'd be afraid of later regretting my choice. I'd fear that a moment of sight might awaken something within me that has long been at rest under the blanket of contentment. I'd be afraid to arouse the desire to see."

Yet days later, the question still haunted me. It nagged at me and began to erode away my contentment, egged on, most likely, by the fact that I had just lost my cane! It had been missing for a week, and every day without it I had grown increasingly frustrated. I was also in the middle of redoing my office, so all the furniture and files were in disarray. That can make even a sighted person grumpy!

I was tired of being blind. I wanted a vacation from it. My morning prayer just before the interview had actually been, "Lord, I know my healing has not been part of your plan so far, but could you give me just a week in Jamaica without blindness? Then I could come home rested and be able to be blind again for another 10 years."

I guess that's why the interview question felt like the sting of a bandage being torn away too quickly. I didn't want to be able to see for a moment. I wanted to see for a while. I wanted to see for a lifetime.

The next day, I showed up at church still grumpy. I wasn't mad at God or even carrying around a portable pity party. I was just tired, worn out. After church, a friend introduced me to someone I had been wanting to meet—Bobby Smith. He's a smart, funny man in his early 50s who oozes attitude! Bobby lost his sight from a gunshot wound while working as a Louisiana law enforcement officer. He was in his 30s when he became totally blind. He described his blindness like a blackness he'd never experienced before. "There's no darkness like it." He inquired about my sight loss. I told him I still had a little light perception. I could tell when it was daylight. He simply sighed a sigh of remembrance. A sigh of pleasure. A sigh of loss.

For me, time was lost in his sigh. My mind raced through the path of discontentment I had traveled all week, and suddenly I became incredibly grateful. What had made me feel grumpy suddenly made me feel grateful. You see, I open my window shade before bed just so the morning sun will fill my window frame. Each sunrise I squint to perceive all I can. For now, I see the light; but I could someday, like Bobby, only see blackness.

As I considered Bobby's darkness, I realized I have little about which to be grumpy. It dawned on me that I've been in Jamaica all along. The little light I enjoy is my Jamaica!

Letting the light remind me of my current blessing instead of warn me of a potential loss is all the vacation from blindness that I need. Being grateful for what I have, rather than grumpy over what I've lost, gives me strength for each sunrise.

God's touch redeems our sorrow, our heartache, and our mistakes. His touch not only redeems us from an orphan's future, but His touch redeems our future, our present, and our past. God's touch redeems everything. The prophet Isaiah said it this way, "He has sent Me ... to provide for those who mourn in Zion; to give them a crown of beauty instead of ashes" (Isa. 61:1-3, HCSB). Only God can redeem so perfectly, so powerfully. For such a touch, we are forever grateful.

Gratitude ... thankfulness ... this may be the quiet giant of all the spiritual disciplines. Sadly, it is underused in many Christian lives and churches. The book of Colossians is a celebration of gratitude. Read the following three verses and summarize what each means to you:

Colossians 2:7 _____

_____

Colossians 3:15 _____

_____

Colossians 4:2 _____

_____

I challenge you to practice the discipline of gratitude daily. In the reality of your present challenges—your illness, your despair, your fear, your ambition, your family, your church, your friends' needs, your enemies' lies—find daily evidence that God's touch redeems everything ... even the heartache. Life is precious; God is good; you are blessed.

Describe in your journal 10 reasons for gratitude today.

In my brief moments with Bobby, I felt God's touch. No one else knew my frustration. No one other than God knew my heartache. And God knew that only a blind man could help me feel the touch of God that redeems everything.

So enjoy your Jamaica today! Open the eyes of your heart, and let the light of gratitude brighten your dark places. Jesus said: " 'I am the light of the world. Whoever follows me will never walk in darkness, but will have the light of life' " (John 8:12).

Jesus is the light shining in our world; we have no better reason for gratitude! Jesus also taught that you and I are the light of the world (see Matt. 5:14). To remind us of the wonderful image we've explored all week, He commanded us to: " 'Put your trust in the light while you have it, so that you may become sons of light' " (John 12:36).

As this book is heading to the publishers, the world has just finished watching the Summer Olympics held in Greece. "The Greeks had a race in their ancient Olympic games that was unique. The winner was not the runner who finished first. It was the runner who finished with his torch *still lit.*"[1]

You and I are sons and daughters of light … children adopted into the light of His presence … children trusted to reflect His brightness in our world today. Father, may you find us, your children, faithful and grateful … with our lights lit until they become indistinguishable in the glorious light of Your presence.

God's touch redeems you. How can you leave the mark of redemption on someone else's life?

Touch Point

WWJD? … Some of you wear that on your wrist. How about wearing it on your actions this week? What would Jesus do if He went to lunch with you today, or rode in your carpool, or sat in the cubicle next to yours? He'd show mercy to those who least deserve it. He would give grace to those who least expect it.

Find someone outside your comfort zone and extend God's mercy and grace by asking how you can pray for them. When you do, others will feel the caress of His nail-scarred hand.

---

[1] J. Stowell, *Fan The Flame* (Chicago: Moody Press, 1986) 32.

Listening Guide

Even beneath the stain of our _____, God sees in us a _____.

God redeemed us with the ultimate price: the precious _____ of _____.

God bought us back because His _____ demands it.

WEEK FOUR
His Sheltering Embrace

As a pastor, the last thing William O. Cushing wanted to lose was his voice. But that's exactly what happened just before his 50th birthday. His passion and livelihood depended on his ability to speak, so with his voice went his identity, ministry, and security. Though I'm sure he asked God for healing and deliverance, God didn't touch him with physical healing. Instead, God extended His everlasting arms and invited William to take shelter there. The psalmist sang of a refuge like this: "You are my hiding place … and surround me with songs of deliverance" (Ps. 32:7).

William Cushing's deliverance was found in such a song—in over 300 of them! Even though he could not speak, his songwriting gave his heart a voice. Cushing wrote compelling and poignant lyrics born out of the shadow of God's sheltering wings. He teamed with the famous evangelistic team of Moody and Sankey as they spread his songs around the world. At age 73, he was moved to contemplate God's shelter in his own quiet suffering when he read, "Keep me as the apple of your eye; hide me in the shadow of your wings" (Ps. 17:8).

Under His Wings I Am Safely Abiding

Under His wings I am safely abiding;
Though the night deepens and tempests are wild,
Still I can trust Him—I know He will keep me;
He has redeemed me and I am His child.

Under His wings, under His wings,
Who from His love can sever?
Under His wings my soul shall abide,
Safely abide forever.

Under His wings, what a refuge in sorrow!
How the heart yearningly turns to His rest!
Often when earth has no balm for my healing,
There I find comfort and there I am blest.

Under His wings, O what precious enjoyment!
There will I hide till life's trials are o'er;
Sheltered, protected, no evil can harm me;
Resting in Jesus I'm safe evermore.

Touch Stones

"He who dwells in the secret place of the Most High
shall abide under the shadow of the Almighty.
He shall cover you with His feathers,
And under His wings you shall take refuge."
Psalm 91:1,4, NKJV

"The Lord is good,
a stronghold in a day of distress;
He cares for those who take refuge in Him."
Nahum 1:7, HCSB

DAY ❀ ONE

Hiding in Him

I'm not sure Jesus ever used office supplies in His parables, but we're going to use some today. Grab three envelopes and a small piece of paper. On one envelope write, "God the Father." On the next, write "Jesus." On the last, write your name. Draw a rock on the piece of paper and write "Jesus" inside the rock. Read the story below, and I'll tell you how to use these items and what they represent.

Several years ago our boys splashed in the ocean of Gulf Shores, Alabama. Two-year-old Conner must have consumed his weight in sand! We hadn't been there long when Clayton ran to me exclaiming, "Mom, hold this! It's the tiniest shell I've ever seen!"

He pleaded with me to protect his newest treasure. The tiny shell was smaller than my smallest fingerprint, barely detectable in the palm of my hand. I settled in my beach chair and dug my toes into the warm sand. The afternoon passed slowly. The wind and tide shifted, but I was immovable! I was queen of the beach—cemented to my throne by sunscreen and sweat.

Without notice, it hit! I may not have moved, but the shoreline did. A giant wave had encroached on my sovereign domain, immersing me in a flood! Sprinkled, dipped, and dunked—I was baptized by all denominational standards!

But what about my son's treasure? Cautiously, I peeled back my clenched fingers to see if the shell had made it through my drenching. Ah, there it was! I could still feel it securely in my grip. I'd done it! My son would never know the peril of this single loving act!

Later, Clayton ran to me. "Mom," he gasped, "do you still have my shell?" "Yes," I proudly replied and recounted my heroism. He giggled, "Thanks, Mom," and ran back into the waves.

My thoughts shifted from my soaked head to bigger things. Like how tiny that shell felt in my hand—and how tiny we are in God's great hand. Colossians 3:3 says, "your life is now hidden with Christ in God," similar to how Clayton's tiny shell was hidden in my hand. Let's use our envelopes to see how securely we are hidden in God's almighty hands.

Read John 14:20. Its last phrase, "I am in you" tells us what happens when you receive Christ—Jesus comes to live in you. Since Jesus has come to live in you, place your "rock of Jesus" drawing in the envelope that bears your name and seal it.

Read Ephesians 1:13. Write on your envelope's closure the name of the One who has sealed you.

Now back to John 14:20 which also says that you are in Christ. That means your life is secure in Christ. So, place your sealed envelope inside the "Jesus" envelope, and seal it too. You are hidden in your Savior, and He is in you! And that's not all!

The phrase, "I am in my Father" means Jesus can never be separated from God. Place the sealed "Jesus" envelope inside the "God the Father" envelope and seal it.

Office supplies have never carried such a spiritual thrill! I hope you can clearly see how Christ is in you and you are safely hidden in God, sealed by His Holy Spirit. But if office supplies don't thrill you, Jesus' words in John 10:28-29 will. This passage is a word picture of the envelope you hold in your hand.

Read John 10:28-29. Explain how securely you are held in the Father's hand.

Nothing can snatch us from the Father's hand. "Neither death nor life, neither angels nor demons, neither the present nor the future, nor any powers, neither height nor depth, nor anything else in all creation, will be able to separate us from the love of God that is in Christ Jesus our Lord" (Rom. 8:38-39). No physical threat, emotional trauma, or spiritual experience can separate us. Life's storms cannot tear us from our secure position in Christ, but emotional, physical, and spiritual storms serve us well. Our response to these storms shows what we believe. Our reaction will reveal our true sense of security.

Read Mark 4:35-41. How does verse 37 describe this storm?

Some storms in life are like that—sudden and fierce. Others are daily and dismal like the drizzle and fog of a dreary London winter.

What about your storm? Describe a recent storm using some of the words below.

Thunderstorm	Flood	Tornado	Earthquake	Hurricane
Tidal wave	Downpour	Windstorm	Black Cloud	Volcano

My storm is like a _____ because ... _____

_____

Storms rock our world. They drench us with a bleakness that makes us feel frightened and alone. That's how the disciples felt in the midst of their storm.

Who was in the boat with them during the storm (v. 38)? _____

Remember your envelopes. During your storm, where were you? Where was Jesus? You may be in a storm, but you are still in God, in Christ, and Christ is in you! You are hidden in Him.

Read Mark 4:38 and see how the disciples reacted to the storm. What did they say when they woke Jesus?

_____

What did you say to God concerning your storm?

_____

How was your response similar to or different from the disciples' reaction?

_____

The disciples had a twofold reaction to the storm and to their sleeping Savior. First, "Don't you care!" When life's winds toss us, we also tend to look up and question God's care. On many occasions through 25 years of blindness, I've asked the same. Let me caution you: asking God a question and questioning God are two different things. The disciples perceived that because Jesus was silent, He didn't care.

My classroom of blindness tests me frequently, but I choose not to question God in a way that doubts His character. He does care, even when He seems silent. He is in your boat with you and in my darkness with me. Don't wrongly represent His character by questioning His care. Instead, ask Him questions like, "Show me, please Lord, that you care; my faith is weak, the storm is fierce. Let me feel your sheltering touch."

Secondly, the disciples assumed the worst not only about their Savior, but also about the storm. "We're going to die!" (Mark 4:38, HCSB®). Have you felt that way? Sometimes it's hard to believe the best and keep hope when your boat is sinking, but Jesus is Lord over the storm! The wind blows at His command (see Ps. 89:9; 107:29; 148:7-8; Prov. 30:4).

God is the authority over life's storms. What or whom did Jesus rebuke in Mark 4:39?

_____

Read the question Jesus asked the disciples in Mark 4:40. Could Jesus be asking you the same question? Do you find your security in a peaceful journey through life or in knowing Jesus is in your boat and you are safely sheltered by His care? Record your thoughts on the answers to these questions in your journal.

DAY ❀ TWO

A Place of Refuge

After her father's death when she was two, Preena lived in a Hindu temple. Her mother sold her to be a temple child, and the frightening rock temple was her entire world. By age seven she had been branded and abused and was to be married to one of the many brutal Hindu gods. But one night Preena overheard two temple women whispering, "A white woman, one of those Christian missionaries," hissed one of the priestesses. "Her name is Amy and she steals children from the temples. She has strong powers from her God, whom they call the Lord Jesus Christ."

Preena hadn't heard much, but a door of hope began to crack. Soon, the literal door of her temple was left open, and she slipped out. Dashing toward the edge of the village, she splashed across a shallow stream. Bewildered, she made her way through a grove of palms and into a village. "Child!" a villager barked. "Where are you going?" "I'm looking for the child stealing Amy," Preena replied. As villagers gathered, they recognized her temple clothes. Since a slave of the gods was never to run away, the Hindu worshipers chased her.

Gasping, she fled and turned down a village street where a white woman stepped out in front of her. Preena stopped! Could this be the child stealer she was looking for? "Help me!" shrieked Preena as she hurled herself into the white woman's arms. "I don't want to be a slave of the gods. I want the Lord Jesus Christ!" The woman's arms tightened around Preena, shielding her from her angry pursuers. The crowd began to shout, "She belongs to the temple!" The temple women screamed, "We paid fifty rupees for her!" But the missionary would not open her protective arms. With unyielding defiance she refused to let the trembling Preena go, and she paid 50 rupees to buy Preena's freedom.

What Amy Carmichael did for Preena, God does for you and me. He is the tower of shelter to which we run. He envelops us with His love and buys us back. Proverbs 18:10 says, "The name of the LORD is a strong tower; the righteous run to it and are safe." His name is our ultimate refuge.

Ancient Jews considered God's name too sacred to speak. It is recorded as *YHWH* in the original Hebrew text. We know this covenant name as *Yahweh* or *Jehovah*. It appears in your Bible in all capitals as *LORD*.[1] Genesis 2:4 records its first occurrence in Scripture, *Yahweh Elohim*. God's covenant name occurs more than 6,000 times in the Old Testament. His name represents both His character and His covenant to us.

God's name is our strong tower of shelter. Consider some of His covenant names. Match each Hebrew covenant name of God to its corresponding English definition.

(Hint: to be sanctified is to be made holy.)

	Hebrew Names of God	English Definition
Genesis 22:14	Jehovah-Jirah	The LORD Who Sanctifies
Exodus 15:22-26	Jehovah-Rapha	The LORD of Hosts
Exodus 17:15	Jehovah-Nissi	The LORD is There
Leviticus 20:8	Jehovah-Mekaddesh	The LORD our Shepherd
Judges 6:24	Jehovah-Shalom	The LORD is my Banner
Jeremiah 23:6	Jehovah-Tsidkenu	The LORD has Healed
Psalm 23:1	Jehovah-Rohi	The LORD will Provide
Ezekiel 48:35	Jehovah-Shamma	The LORD our Righteousness
Isaiah 1:24	Jehovah-Sabaoth	The LORD is Peace

Just like Preena in Amy's arms, the strong tower of God's name safely shelters you. The Old Testament holds a beautiful picture of this very truth. It's called the cities of refuge. Get out your archaeological shovel, and let's dig up some profound artifacts of our faith.

Who ordered the establishment of cities of refuge (Num. 35:9-15)? _____

For whom were the cities of refuge intended (v. 11)? _____

In ancient cities walls provided protection against enemy invaders. Though all powerful ancient cities were walled, certain Hebrew cities were designated as cities of refuge. When God divided the promised land between the tribes of Israel, He gave the Levites 48 towns (Num. 35:7). Six of those towns were designated by God to be cities of refuge (v. 6). Highways and bridges were built providing easy access to these cities (Deut. 19:3).

Though these were Hebrew cities, aliens and foreigners had access to them. These were places of refuge "to which a person who has accidentally killed someone may flee … from the avenger, so that a person accused of murder may not die before he stands trial before the assembly" (Num. 35:11-12). Let's unearth the truth about these ancient cities to learn that Jesus is the true cornerstone of our faith.

Cities of Refuge	Jesus our Refuge
Who had access to the cities (Num. 35:15)?	Who has access to Jesus (John 6:37)?
Who was the accuser (Num. 35:12)?	Who is our accuser (Rev. 12:10)?
What hope did a person find when he fled to a city of refuge (Josh. 20:2-3)?	What hope does a person find in fleeing to Christ (Col. 1:27; Heb. 6:18-19)?
How long could the accused remain secure in the city (Josh. 20:6)?	How long does your High Priest live (Heb. 7:24-26)?

So, how long are you safe in Christ as your refuge? _____

Cities of refuge are a picture of our fortress of salvation. Psalm 28:8 tells us that "The LORD is the strength of his people, a fortress of salvation for his anointed one." God made a place for us when we were needy and accused, by giving us access to Himself. Just as the cities of refuge invited all into their gates, so God invites us.

We all need a city of refuge, because we all stand accused by our enemy. We do have a safe place in our High Priest, Jesus. He is the One who conquered our enemy and ever lives to make intercession for us. Just as Preena discovered, "The eternal God is your refuge, and underneath are the everlasting arms" (Deut. 33:27).

DAY ✿ THREE

The Rock of Protection

Do you ever feel totally spent? Emptied from life's constant demands? Do you sometimes feel your energy is poured out like an endless stream of water pouring into a leaky cup? We all do! Even June Cleaver would have struggled in the 21st century! She would have had to trade in her perfectly starched pinafores for sweats! I doubt her hair and makeup would look so "all together" if she were a part of our world! Most days, I'm lucky if I'm wearing makeup at all! Sometimes, I'm so hurried it seems I open my cosmetic bag, throw it up in the air, and hope the makeup lands in the right place on my face!

Today June Cleaver would drive through a fast-food restaurant after school instead of baking cookies and serving milk! Wally would contemplate body piercing and tattoos while Ward feverishly fingered through Dobson's latest parenting book! Beaver would be obsessed with video games, and June would debate whether to disconnect cable and limit Internet time!

Today's stresses seem overwhelming; we try to be a rock of strength, but our strength is eroded by the merciless tide of demands that washes over us. Sometimes we feel overwhelmed not only because of our schedules and the stresses of life but also because we go to the wrong rock for relief. Here's what I mean: part of the lie we believe is that we are a rock. When life is demanding and stressful, we misguidedly believe we should just "buck up" or "be strong!" God knows that we are prone to this pebble-like mentality. In Deuteronomy 31:20 God told Moses just before his death that the people would soon reject the Mighty Rock only to place their confidence in their own pebbles.

Read Deuteronomy 31:16,21. What does God know in advance about His people?

_____

Did you see that? In verse 21 God points out that He knows our hearts are naturally bent away from Him. He knows we're weak—pebble-like. This weakness shows when we run to other rocks only to discover they're not the gemstones for which we hoped.

The words "Prone to wander, Lord, I feel it. Prone to leave the God I love"[2] may have been written a long time ago, but they still apply today. I do feel it, that continual heart waywardness that draws me away from the God I love so dearly. Yes, those lyrics could be engraved on my heart; they could also have been carved on King Jeroboam's tombstone.

In Jeroboam's day, God's chosen people were divided into two separate kingdoms. Rehoboam ruled the southern kingdom of Judah from the city of Jerusalem, and Jeroboam reigned over the northern kingdom of Israel. Jeroboam feared that his people would shift loyalties if they traveled south to sacrifice at the temple in Jerusalem.

Paraphrase Jeroboam's pebble-like thoughts and actions from I Kings 12:26-30:

_____

Feeling vulnerable and nervous, Jeroboam decided he could substitute the temple of the one true Rock with altars of his own making. With pebble mentality he constructed "gravel" gods and announced to Israel that these gods had brought them from Egypt long ago.

Let's examine what Jeroboam's idols were really made of as you answer the following questions. Mark the word(s) that best represent Jeroboam's choices.

What motivated Jeroboam to build the idols?
❑ Obedience ❑ Confidence ❑ Fear ❑ Trust ❑ Hope ❑ Insecurity

What was the base of the advice Jeroboam sought?
❑ Control ❑ God's Word ❑ Anxiety ❑ Faith ❑ Self-interest ❑ Truth

How did Jeroboam convince the people to worship his idols?
❑ Doubt ❑ Deceit ❑ Convenience ❑ Rationalization ❑ Truth ❑ Sincerity

Jeroboam quickly discovered that he could not confine the Rock within the grip of his control, so he manufactured a couple of more-manageable gods. In so doing, he exchanged the Rock of ages for a few shiny pebbles. That's like our settling for rhinestones when we're offered diamonds.

The words you checked represent Jeroboam's tendency toward choosing pebbles (weakness) rather than the immovable Rock (strength). Pebbles are the things that come naturally to us. The things that feel most comfortable. Things we can control. _An idol is really just our pebbles all thrown into one place, a reflection of our desire to have a refuge within our own strength._

We all desire to find something or someone worthy of our worship. We desperately need to rely on something—even if we have to conjure it up. At the same time we relish our independence. That was Jeroboam's quandary, too. And just like the wayward king, the longer you rely on your pebble strength, the more you'll have a propensity to build an idol. If you don't rely on the revealed God, you'll make a god to rely on.

Read Isaiah 44:8-17 and notice the contrast between the Rock and our pebbles. Record the answers to the following questions in your journal.
- Of what are your idols made?
- Do you want to put your trust in these things?
- How does the quality of this idol compare to the character of God?

DAY ❀ FOUR

Rest in the Shadow

God has secured eternity for those who believe. Jesus is our city of refuge, our safe place to run. He is also our immovable rock, our sure foundation. So, how well do you rest in these bedrock truths?

Take this quiz to assess whether you are counting on your own pebble strength or the mighty rock of God.

	Never	Rarely	Sometimes	Often	Always
I feel safe in God's presence.	1	2	3	4	5
I'm unashamed when I'm in God's presence.	1	2	3	4	5
I'm comfortable being vulnerable toward God.	1	2	3	4	5
I feel protected by God.	1	2	3	4	5
I'm sure God is my defender.	1	2	3	4	5
I am secure in God.	1	2	3	4	5

If you scored mostly 1s and 2s, you're living in an unwalled city. It's time to find your shelter in the immovable Rock. If you scored mostly 2s and 3s, you're in the city with walls, but you're not sure they'll hold up. If you got mostly 4s and 5s, you are living in the safety and delight of a well-fortified refuge.

Early in ministry, I was asked to do a benefit concert for Child Evangelism Fellowship. By that evening, I had recruited just over 100 kids to sing with me. The auditorium was full of proud parents and curious onlookers. Music blared from the sound system as the children streamed in to join me on stage. It was electric! We sang several songs, and then I began to play the keyboard as the kids went to sit with their folks for the rest of the concert.

With every chord I played, the sound worsened. Lifting my foot from the sustain pedal made no difference! I tapped the pedal but got no relief! Five chords still vibrated through the building, sounding more like a haunted house than a Christian concert.

This was terrible! Fear and humiliation ran like ice water through my veins. Hoping to clear the program, I shut off the keyboard and then turned it back on and began to play. One, two, three chords … yikes! It was not fixed! I was reeling inside. It was time for Plan B.

I tried to maintain composure, but I was totally undone. I felt alone on that stage with an unfixable problem. Then I had a brilliant thought … I'll use the piano! My companion walked me to the piano, awkwardly placed near the back of the stage behind a modesty rail. I waited for the sound tech to set up a boom stand and was now ready for the strains of Plan B to resound flawlessly through the sanctuary.

Carefully removing the mike, I began to speak and I gingerly laid my hand on the top beam of the half-wall modesty rail. No sooner had I done this than the railing that extended the entire length of the stage collapsed, sending colossal echoes through the auditorium. The only thing louder than the falling wall crashing against the floor was the panicked sound of the audience gasping and squealing. I felt desperate and helpless. I wanted to walk off that stage and never return. But I faced 20 long minutes of remaining misery.

What happened next has always fascinated me. I had an unexpected and overwhelming urge to call my dad. I imagined him running onto the stage and lifting the railing into place. I imagined his whisper, "It's OK Jenna. I'll take care of this." I wanted more than anything else a place to run and hide—a shelter. A place where to escape humiliation and find protection.

My dad wasn't at the concert, but the memory and reality of my dad was forever imbedded in my heart. He was always my rescuer and my shelter. In my moment of vulnerability and desperation, I longed for his touch. I knew if he were there, this would have all been OK because my dad could fix anything.

Abba Father is your security, strength, and refuge. He will never let you go.

Though you may have never known a dad like that, you do have such a Father. He comes to you when you feel vulnerable and alone. His touch lifts the fallen walls of your hopes and dreams. His arms surround you; His unseen hands can fix anything broken in your life. If your world begins to crumble, He becomes your strength. When you feel exposed and vulnerable, He becomes your refuge, shelter, and hiding place. He will never, never let you go.

I'm sure you've also had a time when things collapsed around you. Describe the circumstances. How did you feel?

_____

_____

This week we've looked at our relationship to God from three perspectives. He is our eternal security, our city of refuge, and the immovable rock. These things provide vivid pictures of the shelter we can find only in a relationship with God Himself. But they just hint at the most important part, and that's the relationship. As a child of God, we are related to Him. We are part of His family. We are His daughters and sons. Now there's a relationship that can never be severed—not by distance, or storms, or even death.

Spend some time reflecting on what we've learned about God's sheltering touch this week. Review the first three days of study, and then consider the words of the psalmist, "You are a shield around me, O LORD; you bestow glory on me and lift up my head" (Ps. 3:3). God lifts fallen sinners, fallen walls, and even willful pebble collectors like me. And He'll do the same for you if you'll just ask.

Write a prayer in your journal as you commit yourself to God's protective care by considering the words of Psalm 94:22.

> "The Lord has become my fortress [of salvation],
>   and my God the rock in whom I take refuge."

Today's lesson is purposefully short so you can have some extra time to meditate on what we've studied this week. God will be your sheltering place of safety, so run to this refuge just like one who fled to the sheltering walls of the city of refuge. No one comes casually sauntering into the shelter of God. Rather, we run to the safety of the everlasting arms.

Let's close out this day by meditating on the following Scripture. How is God inviting you to take shelter in Him?

> "He who dwells in the shelter of the Most High
>   will rest in the shadow of the Almighty" (Ps. 91:1).

DAY ✿ FIVE

Maintain the Walls

I remember the first time I met Beth Moore. We'd both been invited to participate in a conference in south Florida. I was mesmerized by her handling of the Word. She was absolutely genuine and loads of fun. So I picked up the speaking tapes at her table. The message I most wanted from our weekend together was the one on self-control. It resonated with me, and over the years God has used it to continually teach and guide me.

So, when I was preparing this study, I retrieved my beloved tape. As I sat in a comfy chair listening to her introduction, I was struck again by the profound truth she was unfolding. As I continued to listen, something else struck me—the amount of food I had consumed during her message! During the introduction, I ate a handful of dark chocolate. I actually stopped the tape mid-message to get a cup of coffee with French vanilla cream! Near the end of the tape, I found myself dropping leftover Easter jelly beans into my mouth! I paused temporarily throughout her teaching, just long enough to record a verse.

That's when it struck me. As I listened to a message on self-control, I was absolutely out of control! You see, over the years, I've struggled in the area of food! I eat when I'm bored. I eat when I'm mad. I eat when I'm celebrating. I eat when I'm sad! I eat out of curiosity. I eat so my kid's food isn't thrown in the trash, and then, I eat some more for absolutely no searchable reason. I just eat! Several years ago, God began to put His finger on this area of my life. I had true spiritual conviction, godly accountability, and spiritual self-discipline. Sit ups, push ups, more water, and less food led to a smaller version of me.

Well, guess what? My physical appearance may have changed, but my weakness hasn't! I easily fall off the wagon and did I mention, I eat when I'm stressed!? So what does my lack of self-control have to do with maintaining the walls?

The wise writer of Proverbs observed that a man who lacks self-control is like

_____ (Prov. 25:28).

In the margin sketch a well-fortified city and a city with broken down walls.

Ancient cities were only as strong as their walls, so an untended fault provided a weak place the enemy could plunder and attack. It's the same with us. The Hebrew word for wall (*chom wah*) actually means "protection."[3] God has given us a great wall of protection in the form of self-control. Second Peter 1:3 says God has given you all you need for life and godliness. He's given you bricks and mortar to build a wall of self-control, and He's given you a 24/7 maintenance man (the Holy Spirit) to help you keep it strong and fortified.

Write your own definition of self-control (you may check the dictionary if you want).

_____

As Christians we can freely choose how to exercise our will. How does Paul identify self-control according to I Corinthians 6:12?

_____

Paul uses the image of a master and slave as he advises us to develop self-control. A master exerts control over his slave, not the other way around. Are you mastered by anything? Your passions? Your will? What controls you? Do you make wise choices based on truth, or are you enslaved to an unseen overlord? Self-control means not being mastered by anything. The strong, defensive wall of self-control prevents the enemy from coming in to capture and master you and bring you certain disgrace.

What was Nehemiah's primary focus when rebuilding Jerusalem (Neh. 2:17)?

_____

What was the Israelites' first point of entry to Jericho (Josh. 6:20)?

_____

What did Ezekiel first see in the vision God gave him for the future temple (Ezek. 40:5)?

_____

Walls matter! Jerusalem needed a secure wall. The Israelites knew destroying Jericho's wall would give them victory over the entire city. Even the temple in Ezekiel's vision needed a wall. We are also a temple (I Cor. 6:19-20), and the wall that protects us is self-control. When we lack self-control, our protective walls weaken. Satan will enter and make war with us whenever he finds a gap in our self-control. When one area in our lives is out of control, the whole wall is compromised. Satan looks for our weak places and tramples in.

Which of the following are the opposite of self-control? From this list, mark any areas in which you struggle with restraint.
❑ Greed   ❑ Wasting Time   ❑ Gossip   ❑ Overeating   ❑ Pride   ❑ Debt   ❑ Lust
❑ Procrastination   ❑ Self-indulgence   ❑ Laziness   ❑ Careless Words   ❑ Anger

If you're like me, you could probably think of at least a couple more areas in which you could exercise greater discipline. Write them here.

_____

These gaping holes of self-indulgence don't just surface out of nowhere. A lack of self-control may begin as a small fissure, but it can expand into a dangerous breach. I felt a warning alarm go off as I popped jelly beans in my mouth—conviction! Conviction is the feeling of discomfort or guilt we feel over a sin.

Do you feel convicted about something each time you do it, feel it, or think about it? Write about it in your journal.

Read Galatians 5:22-23. From where does self-control come?

_____

What is the job description of the Holy Spirit according to John 16:7-8?

_____

Self-control is a fruit of the Spirit in every believer. The Holy Spirit faithfully convicts us of sin; we cannot possess self-control apart from Him. He convicts us so we'll learn to recognize our sin and exercise self-control, bringing glory to God.

Let's see what your wall of protection looks like.

He will bring _____ to God (John 16:14)

What is the last fruit of the Spirit listed in Galatians 5:23? _____

When he comes, he will _____ the world of _____ (John 16:8)

He will guide you into all _____ (John 16:13)

Your wall of protection is built upon the foundation of truth. The following bricks complete your protective wall.

- The Bricks of Conviction of Sin: Experiencing conviction and admitting guilt is part of maintaining your wall of protection.
- The Brick of Self-Control: Choosing to exercise Spirit led self-control is essential for keeping your wall strong.
- The Brick of God's Glory: You cannot reflect God's glory if your wall is compromised because a brick is missing or damaged.

I know you want to experience the shelter of God in your life, so allow your temple to be surrounded by a wall built on the Chief Cornerstone, brick by brick.

God's touch shelters you. How can you offer similar refuge to someone else?

Touch Point

"You are my hiding place; you will protect me from trouble and surround me with songs of deliverance" (Ps. 32:7). You don't have to be a singer to surround someone with songs of deliverance. Here are some practical ways to extend God's sheltering embrace. Rescue a friend from chaos and take her to your local city of refuge (also known as Starbucks). Refrain from criticism and offer words of encouragement instead. Consciously try to become a trustworthy friend, spouse, or parent so you can be a safe place for someone else—then others will find rest in the sweet music of the Deliverer's song.

[1]"Lexicon Results for *YHWH* (Strong's 03068)," *Blue Letter Bible* [online], [cited 19 October, 2004]. Available from the Internet: *www.blueletterbible.org.*

[2]Robert Robertson, "Come, Thou Fount of Every Blessing," *The Baptist Hymnal* (Nashville: Convention Press, 1991), 16.

[3]James Strong, "Hebrew and Chaldee Dictionary" (2346), *Strong's Exhaustive Concordance of the Bible* (Peabody, MA: Hendrickson Publishers), 37.

Listening Guide

What if the _____ places in life were the

_____ of God?

The uncomfortable places in life can be used by God as His sheltering
embrace to:

- _____ us.

- _____ us.

- _____ us.

Let God's _____ dictate your view of the circumstance.

May your longing to _____ be greater than your longing

to be _____.

The Hand That Guides

By the early 1860's the Civil War was in full swing. Every American heart was heavy with the strain of a war which had torn apart a nation and its people, leaving insecurity in its wake. The pastor of Philadelphia's First Baptist Church sought to reassure his congregation with the truth of God's guidance, and thus their own security. He turned to Psalm 23 one Sunday morning and pronounced, "The important thing is to know that God is leading no matter how or where He leads us."

The morning's message resonated with the congregation. Talk of God's guidance carried over to lunchtime. One discussion took place in a deacon's home where Pastor Joseph Gilmore and his wife had been invited. As families shared their meal, they shared their thoughts about the ways God leads His people. Joseph began to write: "He leadeth me. O blessed thought!" He continued the idea until he concluded that even "death's cold wave I will not flee, since God through Jordan leadeth me!" Then he handed the tattered paper to his wife and never thought of it again.

Several years later, in a New York church, he fingered through a hymnal and much to his surprise he found a hymn bearing his name! What a husband forgets a wife seldom does! Mrs. Gilmore had sent the lunchtime lyrics to a Christian periodical where they had been set to music. Pastor Gilmore would be the first to say, "For those who are led by the Lord, there are often delightful surprises!"

He Leadeth Me

He leadeth me! O blessed
  thought!
O words with heav'nly
  comfort fraught!
Whate'er I do, where'er I be,
Still 'tis God's hand that
  leadeth me!

He leadeth me,
  He leadeth me,
By His own hand He
  leadeth me;
His faithful follower I would be,
For by His hand He
  leadeth me.

Lord, I would clasp Thy hand
  in mine,
Nor ever murmur nor repine,
Content, whatever lot I see,
Since 'tis Thy hand that
  leadeth me!

And when my task on earth
  is done,
When, by Thy grace, the
  vict'ry's won,
E'en death's cold wave I will
  not flee,
Since God through Jordan
  leadeth me!

Touch Stone

"This is what the LORD, your Redeemer,
    the Holy One of Israel says:
I am the LORD your God,
who teaches you for [your] benefit,
who leads you in the way you should go."
Isaiah 48:17, HCSB

DAY ❀ ONE

A Sighted Guide

Standing in a bookstore one afternoon, I met a gentle man named Rosario. His voice smiled as he introduced himself. His companion placed my hand on Rosario's hand as he spoke. Rosario, you see, is blind like me. We bridged the gap of sight with touch and spoke as old friends who had just met. We never pulled our hands away but would sometimes shake them or grip a little tighter. During tender conversation, I placed my remaining hand on our grip. But until our conversation ended, the touch lingered and reassured each of us that the other was still there.

Touch reassures us we are not alone in the darkness. Touch grounds and guides us. We are all in darkness at some time. We need God's touch to orient, reassure, and guide us.

Read Ephesians 5:8. What does the verse say about you and the darkness?

❑ I was the darkness.　❑ The darkness surrounded me.　❑ Darkness blinded me.

Jesus is the light. Without Him, we're not just in darkness, we are darkness.

Our culture says a lot about darkness through its clichés. Describe what each of the following means:

The blind leading the blind _____

A shot in the dark _____

Love is blind _____

I'm in the dark about that _____

You've just written a good definition of darkness. Darkness involves ignorance, aimlessness, lack of understanding and direction, and foolishness.

According to John 11:10; 12:35; Romans 1:21; and Ephesians 4:18, what characterizes the life of a person in darkness?

_____

_____

_____

_____

What is the only remedy for such darkness? Is it philosophy, psychology, or enlightenment? Is it therapy, education, or self-actualization? No. Simply put, the only remedy for darkness is light! Just as human touch guides me in my physical darkness, God's touch guides me out of my spiritual darkness. His touch isn't skin on skin. No, His touch is light.

What does each of these clichés about light mean?

Shed some light _____

The light of day_____

In the light _____

The light came on_____

Compare the definitions you wrote by the darkness clichés to those you listed about light. Light brings understanding, illumination, revelation, and even warmth.

God's light brings the same to us. Let's examine many facets of God's guiding light. Describe how these verses characterize light:

Psalm 27:1 _____

Psalm 119:105 _____

John 8:12 _____

2 Corinthians 4:6 _____

1 John 1:7 _____

When as a 15-year-old girl my world became dark, I had to find a way to navigate. I relied heavily on my dad's guiding touch. He made me feel most secure. His hand was always steady, his touch gentle, and he always pointed me in the right direction.

Our Father God does the same for us. His Word points us in the right direction. Walking in His light keeps us in step with each other. You see, "You were once darkness, but now you are light in the Lord. Live as children of light" (Eph. 5:8). God's light was the touch you received to guide you out of your darkness. Yet as children of light, our path can still become dark at times. Confusion, stress, tragedy, and even mediocrity are all difficult shadows to navigate without a guiding light.

Ask God to quicken your mind to recognize His light. Journal how God's truth, gospel, and salvation have guided you. Record in your journal this week the times you clearly notice the invisible hand of God guiding you as He floods light into your darkness.

DAY ❀ TWO

A Perplexed Prophet

Yesterday we saw that we were at one time darkness and God's touch rescued us. We acknowledged that even as children of light we experience darkness and its disorientation. Believe me, my life is a walking illustration! Open the car door and let me out most anywhere, and you will have one disoriented lady. Without physical sight or someone to guide me, I would have no idea which way to turn. There's nothing amazing about that. It's what you would expect. What's amazing to me is how we usher in our own disorienting darkness when we're disobedient to the Lord or when we reject His counsel and guidance. The confusion rolls in like fog off the bay, and the darkness is profound.

I can't think of a better example than a prophet named Jonah. By deliberately turning his back on God, he ran into a darkness beyond what most of us could even imagine. This is not just a fish story—it describes you and me and how God pulls us from the darkness that swallows us and guides us back to the path of His purpose.

By examining Jonah's story and your story as told in God's Word, we'll begin to see how God's touch guides us.

Read the following verses, then fill in the actions or words of each character.

The Story of God and Jonah (Jonah 1)	The Story of God and You
God _____ (vv. 1-2)	God _____ (Deut. 5:29)
Jonah _____ (v. 3)	I _____ (Ps. 78:10,17)
God _____ (v. 4)	God _____ (Nah. 1:3)
Jonah _____ (vv. 7-9,15)	I _____ (Prov. 1:32-33)
God _____ (v. 17)	God _____ (Ps. 78:37-39)

I'm sure you recognized Jonah's story, but did you recognize your own? Read the second column aloud and notice that your story ends with God's mercy.

For Jonah, mercy was a giant fish with a man-sized appetite! When Jonah was cast into the ocean, the story should have ended, right? But, "He does not treat us as our sins deserve or repay us according to our iniquities" (Ps. 103:10). Instead, God swallows us up in His mercy when we are sinking in sin, just as He did for His rebellious prophet.

Before you think you would never do what Jonah did, consider his motivation. Jonah had watched his countrymen taken away as slaves, women and children killed, and his beloved land stolen by brutal Assyrians. And then the unthinkable happened. God called Jonah to go to the capital city of Nineveh and preach repentance.

When life's twists and turns seem to bend with unexpected kinks, we can become distracted and disoriented. I'm sure at one point, Jonah had the same focus as God did—after all, Jonah was a prophet. Preaching repentance was what he did! But disobedience was pretty clear evidence that Jonah had shifted his gaze.

Connect the words below by drawing lines to words that reveal the focal point of either Jonah or God. Notice the contrast between God's focus and Jonah's.

	GOD	
Love		Fear
Anger		Hatred
Forgiveness		Prejudice
Justice		Grace
Redemption		Repentance
Self-preservation		Compassion
Mercy	**JONAH**	Stubbornness

Throughout Jonah's journey, God focused on mercy. Jonah's nearsightedness landed him in a fish's belly. In that place of darkness Jonah finally saw the light. What some would call fish guts, Jonah called a prayer closet! He must have knelt among the catch of the day and glimpsed God's goodness. The prophet shifted his gaze from his problem to his Provider. He became thankful for the holy life preserver God had mercifully prepared.

In Jonah's blackest moment, the light of God's Word began to orient him. The Bible records Jonah's prayer in that dreadful place. Throughout the pages of Scripture, you will encounter all kinds of prayers, on all kinds of occasions, and in all kinds of places. But this has to be the first recorded prayer from under the sea.

Read Jonah 2. This prayer is a series from the Psalms. Even in deep disorientation, God's Word will be a lamp to our feet and a light for our path (see Ps. 119:105).

Compare the Psalms with Jonah's prayer. Write your own psalm as a prayerful response.

Jonah's Prayer	Corresponding Psalm	Your Response
Jonah 2:2	Psalm 120:1	
Jonah 2:3	Psalm 42:7	
Jonah 2:4	Psalm 31:22	
Jonah 2:5	Psalm 69:1	
Jonah 2:7	Psalm 142:3	
Jonah 2:8	Psalm 31:6	
Jonah 2:9	Psalm 3:8; 116:17-18	

When we are in the darkness of disobedience and rebellion, God can restore us to the path of His purpose. Disobedience and rebellion are not reserved for headstrong prophets; all of us are subject to going our own way. I've taken some wacky turns on my life's journey. Why? Because I set up my own compass. Sometimes I don't follow God or respond to His guidance. Have you done the same?

You may have a specific area in your life in which you are not walking in obedience. Or, you may have an area of rebellion. Ouch!

Check the box below which most closely represents your walk with Christ. Then, in your journal, write a prayer of confession to your Father God.

❏ I struggle constantly with disobedience in one area of my life.
❏ I'm not consistent in my walk of obedience.
❏ I know of no area of disobedience in my current walk.

Rebellion and disobedience deserve death. Even if you are in an uncomfortable place due to your own choices, be thankful like Jonah. Sometimes God allows us to be swallowed up by His mercy for our own protection. Shift your gaze from your problem to your Provider. Allow His touch to guide you back to truth and His good purposes for your life.

DAY ❋ THREE

A Misguided Monarch

How lost in darkness must you be before you're beyond help and hope? What if you had rebelled not once, as Jonah did, but had lived in complete rebellion all your life? That's a different matter—or is it? Would you be overwhelmed to know that God will go a long, long way to touch someone who is lost and can't find the way home?

Manasseh, son of King Hezekiah of Judah, inherited the throne from his father. The thirteenth king of Judah, Manasseh reigned longer than any other Hebrew king. Unfortunately, not only his long reign put Manasseh into the record books.

According to 2 Chronicles 33:9, what other distinction does Manasseh hold?

_____

Before you think he simply cheated on his taxes, let's consider the details of Manasseh's story. Read 2 Chronicles 33:1-8. List King Manasseh's evil ways:

_____   _____

_____   _____

_____   _____

_____   _____

As far as Judah was concerned, Manasseh was one vile package. Many believe Hebrews 11:37 refers to the callous king's having the prophet Isaiah put to death. Clearly, Manasseh was a bad dude! Jonah received God's word yet struggled with a temporary lapse in obedience, but Manasseh practiced all-out rejection of God. He turned his back on his godly heritage and hardened his heart as he adopted false gods and evil practices.

Just as Jonah's rebellion led to disorientation, so did Manasseh's rejection of God. However, God's righteous judgment caught up to him. (By the way, it always does.)

What was the outcome of Manasseh's rejection (2 Chron. 33:10-11)?

_____

_____

The Assyrians dragged away the once-proud king of Judah with a hook in his nose. Hezekiah's son was held captive by a mighty military state—and utterly without hope.

When we choose to reject God, we eventually end up like Manasseh—captive, bound, and chained by feelings of hopelessness. Our hard hearts lead us to a place of utter desperation. So how, then, do we become oriented in that kind of darkness? How do we find freedom from the bondage our rejection has created?

According to 2 Chronicles 33:12, what did Manasseh do?

_____

Manasseh humbled himself and prayed. The humble person doesn't have to announce, "I am humble." Humility has its own vocabulary.

Pick out the words indicating humility spoken by the following people.

Jacob (Gen. 32:10) _____

King Saul (1 Sam. 9:21) _____

King David (2 Sam. 7:18) _____

King Solomon (1 Kings 3:7) _____

John the Baptist (Matt. 3:14) _____

The centurion (Matt. 8:8) _____

Paul (1 Tim. 1:15) _____

Write a prayer in your journal confessing any areas of your life where these words of humility don't apply. Pay attention as you consider and write these since a high correlation usually exists between the areas in which we reject God and the areas in which we are not humble. Do you see that in your life?

Read Micah 6:8, and ask God to show you how you can walk humbly with Him. Jot down your thoughts in your journal.

Manasseh was far from home, deep in the bowels of some awful dungeon, possibly chained to the wall, robbed of all light and hope. Almost ...

At a moment that must have been close to utter despair, the captive king remembered something from his long-ago innocence. Maybe it was a psalm or a prayer. Maybe it was a promise. Whatever it was, he turned his heart to the God of his father. And he exercised just enough humble faith to invite God's guiding touch into his life.

Read 2 Chronicles 33:13. What was God's response to Manasseh's humility?

_____

We don't know what Manasseh prayed, but since we know he greatly humbled himself, his prayer must have contained words similar to those you listed. Fortunately, we have a brief record of Manasseh's reign after God restored Him.

Read 2 Chronicles 33:14-17. What kind of offerings did Manasseh give the Lord?

_____

The peace offering (or fellowship offering) is the third of the five sacrifices of the people of Israel (Lev. 3:6-7). The peace offering was an expression of freewill and could also be offered to fulfill a special vow (Lev. 22:21). Each offering had special significance, and this one invited the peace of God. The thank offering was part of the peace offering.

Manasseh gave these offerings because he had been restored, though he was unworthy. Why would God touch this heathen king? The same reason He touches you and me. It's just what He does. Remember, you and I, in our unredeemed state, rejected God. We've also been held captive by our sin. Though we are unworthy, the sacrifice of Jesus was offered for us. Oh, how can you keep from giving thanks? What a peace!

Pause and offer thanks to God for His touch that guides you in the path of peace.

Are you in bondage because you've rejected God's truth? Humbly call on God. He stands ready to restore you. He listens in anticipation of your humble cry for help. Pardon me for sounding like Bob the Tomato, but here's what I hope you learned today:

1. A lack of humility reflects a rejection of God and His truth.
2. Don't reject God or His truth. Instead, receive.
3. Humble yourself; God will respond.
4. Give thanks, for God is your peace.

DAY ❀ FOUR

The King with a Capital "I"

As pagan kings go, Nebuchadnezzar is definitely one of my favorites. At least, he's one of the most intriguing. See what I mean as you respond to these true or false statements.

True	False	
❏	❏	Nebuchadnezzar was the fourteenth king of Israel (Dan. 1:1).
❏	❏	Nebuchadnezzar worshiped false gods (Dan. 1:2).
❏	❏	King Nebuchadnezzar erected an image of his mother-in-law and made his people worship it (Dan. 3:1).
❏	❏	Nebuchadnezzar did not need therapy for low self-esteem (Dan. 4:28-30).
❏	❏	Shadrach, Meshach, and Abednego voted King Nebuchadnezzar "Monarch of the Year" (Dan. 3:19-20).
❏	❏	Nebuchadnezzar was a harsh and evil conqueror (Jer. 39:1,3-8).

Nebuchadnezzar was the notorious king of Babylon. He began his reign 600 years before the King of kings stepped onto our planet. He reigned over Babylon for 43 years. During his tenure he beautified and fortified his great city. Temples, waterways, and the wondrous hanging gardens (one of the seven wonders of the ancient world) were all of his royal doing! King Nebuchadnezzar was a proud and boastful man. He was the greatest and most powerful of all the Babylonian kings. However, that all changed one fateful day.

Explain what happened according to Daniel 4:30-33.

_____

_____

To put it simply, Nebuchadnezzar lost it. For seven years, Nebuchadnezzar took on the lifestyle and demeanor of a beast. From a palace to a pasture, this confused king made his abode among the cows and donkeys. Talk about disoriented! That's what pride does.

Jonah's rebellion, Manasseh's rejection, and Nebuchadnezzar's pride flung them into darkness. Pride makes clear vision pretty difficult. It makes the spotlight on "me, myself and I" shine so brightly that everything and everyone else is in the shadows. King Nebuchadnezzar wasn't the only monarch who groped through the maddening darkness of his pride. The following four kings all faced pride-revealing situations.

Read their individual accounts. What makes you think they struggled with pride?

King Sennacharib of Assyria (Isa. 10:12) _____

King of Tyre (Ezek. 28:2,4-5,17) _____

King Uzziah of Judah (2 Chron. 26:16) _____

King Hezekiah of Judah (2 Kings 20:12-18) _____

If those four kings were speaking in today's vernacular, they would have said: "My way, my looks, my brains, my rule, my skill, my clout, my stuff." Sounds a lot like King Nebuchadnezzar to me! Do you ever sound like that? Believe me, Queen Jennifer does! We all struggle. It's ugly, and it's dangerous. Just look what it did to those kings. Let's examine the pride-revealing issues.

Write the following sentence in your journal and insert the words that tell the area(s) in which you struggle with pride. This is tough, but it's worth the discomfort when you consider the potential consequences. Hang in there with me; I'm doing this too!

I struggle with pride when it comes to my …

home	career	kids	looks	possessions
status	money	talent	intelligence	education
car	clothes	position	friends	accomplishments

Proverbs 11:2; 18:12; and James 4:6 disclose the perils of pride. Read those verses and continue to respond in your journal.

How can pride bring you low? If, for example, your issue is your position, it might bring you low when somebody gets more recognition than you do. Now take that tidbit and make it your own!

Pride drove King Nebuchadnezzar crazy, and it can, in many ways, do the same to us. That's why I asked you to deal with it privately in your journal. Pride is maddening because it's insatiable. It always wants more. Better position. Higher achievements. Nicer clothes. More money. Which leads to more pride.

Whether it's your career, home, or accomplishments, lay your source of pride down on the altar. Don't allow those things to remain a source of pride. Instead, let them become a source of thanksgiving. Did you catch that? Don't possess that which you are proud of. Instead, offer it to God and thank Him for letting you borrow it.

Complete the following sentences:

I offer to God my _____

I am a steward of my _____

I am thankful for my _____

Somewhere in the middle of a barren field, Nebuchadnezzar had a moment of sanity and he raised his eyes toward heaven.

Read his words of thanks in Daniel 4:34-37. Read verse 37 again and insert your name in this declaration of praise. Record your own offering of thanks to God in your journal.

Nebuchadnezzar's darkness was ushered in by his own pride. God's guiding touch restored his sanity and his kingdom. God does the same for you and me. When we find ourselves in a state of prideful darkness, God guides us back to the light of His kingdom. A heart filled with gratitude does not have room for pride. So be thankful!

DAY ❀ FIVE
Get Those Unmentionables Out of Your Life

Girl's weekend has existed for about 10 years—beach condos, New York City hotels, and even our homes have hosted our yearly estrogen-charged escapes! This year, Katharyn, Lori, and I chose Kansas City for our latest girl's weekend. We arrived late Thursday night. My expectations and excitement were brimming—the only thing I anticipated more than the shopping was our lovely suite's restroom. It had been a long drive!

After checking in, I raced into our bathroom and quickly shut the door—well, I tried to shut the door. Something had lodged beneath it, and the door was jammed. I reached down to dislodge the assumed washcloth, grasped the wad of fabric, and screamed! It was men's underwear! Katharyn and Lori rushed in for a "sight" inspection. When Katharyn screamed "Gross!" and Lori moaned, I knew for certain … I held an anonymous man's underwear.

We all marched from the restroom to the phone. I pressed zero and when the young man at the front desk asked, "How may I help you?" I exploded, "There's men's underwear in my bathroom." He awkwardly responded, "I'm sorry, ma'am." I stammered and stuttered until he interrupted with, "I'll send someone up." And so, we stood near the door as far from the plague as possible and waited for the attendant.

Five, ten, twenty minutes—time passed, but no one came to our rescue. Finally I could no longer hold back my righteous indignation! Girl's weekend had been violated! Testosterone, remote controls, football, and yes, men's underwear were strictly forbidden!

As Katharyn and Lori sat by the door, I quickened my pace back to the bathroom, picked up my cane, and stabbed those "whitey tighties" with the tip of my walking stick. Like a speargun in the belly of its prey, I proved to that mass of cotton who was boss! I marched proudly toward the door with cane pointed toward the heavens and commanded, "Katharyn, open the door!" She did, and out flew the skivvies into the hallway. We roared with laughter as I again picked up the phone and told the delinquent desk clerk that the underwear was now in the hall. Katharyn watched from the window and sure enough, hotel personnel arrived in five minutes to disinfect the hallway!

So, what's the point? Some things in our lives simply don't belong. For a daughter of the King to hold onto such unmentionables as pride, rebellion, or rejection simply won't do. These things get in the way of what God has planned for you. Instead of enjoying the pleasure of the palace as God intended, you end up in a pasture. Instead of experiencing the fulfillment of the purpose to which God has called you, you find yourself in the belly of a fish with seaweed wrapped around your head. Rather than finding delight in the truths of your godly heritage, you discover that you're chained in a dungeon of unintended consequences. That's when it's time for real righteous indignation.

Don't hover and huddle by the door, waiting for sin to march itself out of your life. Instead, march forward by faith. Stare it down; use the tools God gave you to conquer it; and then, fling it out of your life! You might need someone to open the door for you or walk beside you, but don't let precious plans and your purposeful life be derailed by something that doesn't belong. Now, my friend, I must admit I'm way too experienced at sin removal! And I've found two tools specifically that God provides to help me. So just in case you discovered a few unmentionables through this week's study that need to be "flung," let me open the door and guide you through it.

Today we'll discover two tools to help you get rid of these unmentionables. The first tool might be a surprise. It's the law. Yikes! Don't be nervous. Let's just see what it does.

What is the purpose of the law as a tool?

Romans 3:20 _____

Romans 5:13 _____

Galatians 3:24 _____

The law is a tool that leads to life and clarity. Here's why: It clearly reveals our unmentionables. It makes us aware of our sin, exposes our need, and leads us to Jesus' gracious and guiding nail-pierced touch. If you're like me, this week you've probably recognized some sin in your life. Take a moment now to acknowledge that sin to your heavenly Father. As you confess your sin, don't forget that the nature of confession means that you agree with God—what He calls dirt, you call dirt.

> The law leads to life and clarity. Repentance leads to a new direction.

Read 1 John 1:9 and thank God for the forgiveness He gives.

The second tool in the box is repentance. God empowers us to turn from sin and fling it out of our lives. The Greek word for repentance is *metanoia*. It means "a changing of one's mind or direction." So, in which direction are you walking?

On each of these scales place an arrow that indicates your position:

Rebellion (Hos. 14:9) ❋ ——————————— ❋ Obedience (Deut. 8:6)

Rejection (Prov. 14:2b) ❋ ——————————— ❋ Acceptance (Prov. 14:2a)

Pride (Rom. 12:3) ❋ ——————————— ❋ Humility (Phil. 2:5,8)

Proverbs 28:13 says, "He who conceals his sins does not prosper, but whoever confesses and renounces them finds mercy." When Jonah came to the intersection of repentance, he made a U-turn (Jonah 2:4). When Manasseh was on the road toward rejection, he came to a dead-end and did an about-face (2 Chron. 33:12-13). And Nebuchadnezzar did a complete 180° (Dan. 4:34).

   Do you need to change your mind? To turn around and walk in the other direction? To wield this tool of repentance? Write your prayer of repentance in your journal. God will show you mercy, and you too will feel His guiding touch.

When you think about it, God's touch is light that guides us, mercy that rescues us, restoration that honors us … it's grace. The tool of the law guides us to God's grace through Jesus Christ. The tool of repentance guides us to a restored relationship with God through the grace of Jesus Christ. God's amazing grace guides us through the twists and turns of this life. Ultimately, God's grace leads us from darkness to light. In the words of John Newton, "Tis grace that brought me safe thus far and grace will lead me home."

God's touch guides you. How can God use you to extend His touch?

Touch Point
Some people in your life experience darkness—sometimes it's confusion, sometimes tragedy, sometimes mediocrity, and even stress! How can you sprinkle light into their darkness? You don't know when you'll be confronted with the need to guide someone. Be prepared by memorizing God's Word. Develop a lifestyle of hiding God's Word in your heart. The next time a need arises, you'll be able to shed some light on someone else's path. (Ps. 119:105)

[1]"Lexicon Results for *metanoia* (Strong's 5278)," *Blue Letter Bible* [online], [cited 15 October, 2004]. Available from the Internet: *www.blueletterbible.org.*

Listening Guide

God's light is:

- _____ (John 8:32; Gal. 5:1).

- _____ and _____ (Heb. 13:5).

- _____ (Isa. 43:2).

- eternal _____ (Isa. 49:16).

God's _____ is light to our feet (Ps. 119:105).

The entrance of God's Word brings _____ (Ps. 119:130, KJV).

_____ causes you to walk in darkness rather than being

led by His _____.

_____ Himself is our Light.

Shaped by His Hand

Thomas Chisholm was born in a log cabin in 1866. A self-educated Kentucky farm boy, Thomas often referred to himself with the phrase "Aw, I'm just an old shoe!" As a self-proclaimed "old shoe," he apparently knew something about walking in the steps of Jesus as you'll see from the words he wrote in this old hymn:

O to Be Like Thee!

O to be like Thee! Blessed Redeemer,
This is my constant longing and prayer;
Gladly I'll forfeit all of earth's treasures,
Jesus, Thy perfect likeness to wear.

O to be like Thee! O to be like Thee,
Come in Thy sweetness, come in Thy fullness--
Stamp Thine own image deep on my heart.

O to be like Thee! Full of compassion,
Loving, forgiving, tender and kind;
Helping the helpless, cheering the fainting,
Seeking the wand'ring sinner to find.

O to be like Thee! While I am pleading,
Pour out Thy Spirit, fill with Thy love,
Make me a temple meet for Thy dwelling,
Fit me for life and heaven above.

Thomas was a humble, hard working young man who began teaching in a rural school at age 16. Over the years he was skillfully shaped like clay in the hands of the Divine Potter, and when he was 27, he wrote the beautiful words you just read. His heart's desire was to be like the Savior, and like Jesus, Chisholm eventually became a traveling preacher. Later, with debilitating health constraints, he must have felt the gentle pressure of the Potter's hand in response to his lyrical plea. God was molding him to look like His Son. Throughout his life, Thomas displayed more qualities of Christ than he ever realized, for the one who described himself as an "old shoe" truly possessed the lovely feet of one who bears good news (Isa. 52:7).

Touch Stones

"But now, O LORD, You are our Father,
We are the clay, and You our potter;
And all of us are the work of Your hand."
Isaiah 64:8, NASB

"But he knows the way that I take;
when he has tested me, I will come forth as gold."
Job 23:10

DAY ONE

Refined, Not Defined

My assistant's voice trailed off as she finished reading the final words of the article about me in a magazine. This was our first chance to read the results. The flatness in Katie's voice mirrored my own disappointment.

"Do you like it?" she asked.

"It's okay." I was quiet for a minute before I blurted out my real feelings. "Katie, I don't like it! I don't like it at all!"

"Me either!" she replied. "It's about your blindness; it's not about you."

Katie was on target. Many articles have been written about my journey into darkness, but this one seemed to exploit the enigma of sight loss. It seemed to paint me as part of a circus sideshow.

I'll be honest: I don't like to be defined by my blindness. To me, it's just another facet of who I am. I'm a woman. I'm a wife. I'm a mother. I'm a highlighted brunette (thanks to L'Oreal convincing me that I'm worth it!). I'm 5'3" (almost). I'm trying to be more like Jesus. And yes … I'm blind.

I resented being characterized by my blindness because my blindness does not define me. I embrace my blindness because it refines me. God has permitted this hardship in my life. God uses it as His hands to shape, mold, and train me. I believe God moved on my life with the finesse of an artist and the practiced hand of a sculptor. He allowed me to experience this affliction from the age of 15, not to define me but to refine me.

God's Refining Fire

The Bible uses many powerful images to help us understand life's hardships. Let's examine three of them today. The Bible typically pairs the image of refining with fire.

Read these Scriptures that talk about God's acts as those of a refining fire: Isaiah 48:10; Zechariah 13:9; Malachi 3:2; and 1 Corinthians 3:13. In your journal, summarize from these passages the purpose of God's refining fire.

God's fire melts away impurities like a smelter purifies metals. We don't casually warm ourselves next to such a fire, but we are wise to allow it to complete its work. In the presence of God's fire, He purifies and strengthens us.

As you reflect on God's refining fire, think of one difficulty or hardship you've faced recently. Then, answer the following questions in your journal:

1. How did you experience God's comfort?
2. What was God revealing that you needed to confront in your life?
3. How did your response demonstrate your faith?
4. What do you know about God now that you didn't know before this hard time?
5. What do you know about yourself now that you didn't know before?

God's Shaping Hands

God gave Jeremiah another powerful image.

Read this vivid object lesson in Jeremiah 18:1-6 and answer the questions below:

What does the clay represent? _____

Who does the potter represent? _____

How does this image help us understand God's purposes in our times of difficulty

or suffering? _____

The potter and clay image is two-sided. On one side, God makes clear to His people that their actions, made independently of God's plans, have dire consequences.

How does Jeremiah 19:1-2,10-11 combine pottery and God's judgment?

_____

God's discipline becomes direct when our hard times result from our stubborn pursuit of our own plans, but one thing is constant. Whether God is shaping the clay or reshaping it because it has become marred, the clay is "in his hands." The potter works with it or reworks it with the best in mind (Jer. 18:4).

Times of pressure, trials, or heartaches can produce a beautiful reshaping of your life through the careful, measured pressure of God's own hands. The Scriptures below are just a few that remind us of the love and security delivered by God's hands.

Match the reference with the summary of each verse:

Psalm 37:24	His hands guide us
Psalm 139:10	We cannot be taken out of His hands
John 10:28	His hands hold us up

God's Fatherly Discipline

Hebrews says, "Endure hardship as discipline; God is treating you as sons" (12:7). You may think discipline means punishment, but to assume hardship is God's punishment is to misunderstand His character. The same Greek word used for "discipline" appears in the two verses in the margin.

Circle the word in each margin verse that most closely means *discipline.*

Training may not be pleasant at times, but it is not punishment! All these words come from one Greek word, *paideia,* a word that means: "1) the whole training and education of children. It also includes the training and care of the body. 2) whatever in adults also cultivates the soul, esp. by correcting mistakes and curbing passions."[1]

God works through the difficult situations in our lives to discipline, nurture, and instruct us. Sometimes God is most merciful when He allows us to experience the pressures and pain of heartache because it disciplines, instructs, and nurtures us. I'm thankful God doesn't remove His hand from the clay of my life too soon, leaving me misshapen. I'm thankful He is nurturing me through patient teaching. I'm thankful He carefully positions me near His refining fire until I begin to reflect His glory.

Journal a prayer thanking God for His discipline during a difficult time.

Phillips Brooks once said, "O, do not pray for easy lives; pray to be stronger men! Do not pray for tasks equal to your powers; pray for powers equal to your tasks. Then the doing of your work shall be no miracle, but you shall be a miracle."[4] What are you willing to accept in your life to be a living miracle?

"Fathers, do not exasperate your children; instead, bring them up in the training and instruction of the Lord." **Ephesians 6:4**

"All Scripture is God-breathed and is useful for teaching, rebuking, correcting and training in righteousness."

2 Timothy 3:16

DAY ✿ TWO

We Four and No More: Part 1

God often uses affliction to mold, teach, and nurture us. Continue reflecting on God's refining touch by reading Hebrews 10:32-34.

What kinds of difficulties are described in these verses? List them below:

_____

Circle the one that would be the most difficult for you and explain why:

_____

Notice the timing of these difficulties. According to verse 32, when did they come?

_____

> "No discipline seems
>
> pleasant at the
>
> time, but painful.
>
> Later on, however,
>
> it produces a
>
> harvest of right-
>
> eousness and peace
>
> for those who have
>
> been trained by it."
>
> **Hebrews 12:11**

These verses address people under great strain from persecution because they had "received the light" (v. 32)—because they were professing Christians.

Did the difficulty you circled come from your commitment to live out your faith?

❑ yes ❑ no explain: _____

Whatever the source of our difficult times, the writer of Hebrews knew that people grow weary in the midst of hardship. Our hands begin to hang to our sides; our knees begin to wobble. We begin to look over our shoulder and think about turning back. That's why he encouraged worn-out believers with the message of Hebrews 12:11.

Circle words in the margin verse that encourage you. Think back to the difficulty you journaled about yesterday. What can you apply from this verse to that difficulty? Record your thoughts in your journal.

According to Hebrews 12, pressures and trials will force us into one of four identities. I call them the flippant fatalist, the frail fainter, the faithful follower, and the fruitful finisher.

1. The flippant fatalist

This person pretends to disregard hardship, passing it off as the law of averages. Doris Day hit the charts singing, "Que sera, sera, Whatever will be, will be." Instead of receiving God's message within suffering, the fatalist simply passes it off with a sigh and a shrug. The short hop from "flippant fatalist" to "willing martyr" puts us in danger of becoming passive in the midst of trouble, rarely seeking options, and failing to seek God, His comfort, or His presence.

The writer of Hebrews specifically warns us, "Do not make light of the Lord's discipline" (12:5). Don't regard casually what God is doing through your trials and pressing circumstances. Instead of assuming our suffering is meaningless, we need God to guide our efforts to discern His message. Then we can learn the lesson of our affliction.

Instead of being flippantly fatalistic, we can be fortified in our faith. We often read Job's story to discover how to live with the worst of life's circumstances. He had more reasons than most to be passively victimized by his suffering. But was he?

How did Eliphaz explain Job's suffering (Job 5:17-18)?

_____

Eliphaz is accurate theologically. However, he presumes that he is accurate situationally. He outlined one understanding of suffering but could not know whether it applied to Job's situation. God alone possesses this knowledge, and He may or may not reveal it.

Read all of Job 23. Check the statement that best expresses Job's heart cry:
❏ I deserve the suffering I'm experiencing.
❏ If I could find God, I know He'd hear me and help me.
❏ God doesn't care about me … that is quite clear.

Does one of these statements summarize the cry of your heart about hardships? Circle that statement, or write in the margin what would be more accurate for you.

Job seems to be making the middle statement above. His words carry no flippancy. He is suffering, yes … and he is seeking what he needs most in his suffering, the assurance of God's presence and power. Surely one of the most faith-filled declarations of Scripture is Job's when he said: "God may kill me, but still I will trust him" (13:15, CEV).

2. The frail fainter

Many Christians become fainters when the fire of trials gets hot. We collapse and quit! We pick up our marbles and go home. One preacher calls this the "crybaby reaction." If you listen closely, you can hear the frail fainter lamenting: "Why did this happen to me? I can't take it anymore; it's just not worth living the Christian life if this is how it is."

Read in the margin what God has to say to the frail fainter in Hebrews 12:5. Underline the final phrase of the verse.

> "You have forgotten that word of encouragement that addresses you as sons: 'My son, do not make light of the Lord's discipline, and do not lose heart when he rebukes you.' "
>
> **Hebrews 12:5**

This strong command is like Paul's word to the Corinthian Christians.

Read 2 Corinthians 4:16 and record the phrase that mirrors the one in Hebrews 12:5:

_____

Don't lose heart! Don't lose hope. If you were writing a letter to the Hebrew believers or Corinthian church, what words would you use to encourage them not to give up?

_____

If you skim 2 Corinthians 4, you'll find Paul was being punished by circumstances, scheming officials, and a grueling schedule—all of which took a terrible physical toll. "Outwardly," he said, "we are wasting away" (v. 16). And he offered an intriguing image: "We have this treasure in jars of clay" (v. 7). Paul understood that eternal God chooses to reside in temporary vessels—you and me!—and that we easily chip and crack.

See why this did not discourage Paul but rather energized him. Read 2 Corinthians 4: 10-11, and record the phrase that concludes each verse:

_____

Did you find the phrase, "so that the life of Jesus may also be revealed in our mortal body"? I heard a pastor say once that if the clay jar that is our life is cracked and chipped, even broken, then the glory of God can shine through us. So the question for you and me would be: "Is this reason enough for me to remain faith-filled and hopeful during difficult times, so that God's glory and Jesus' life can be revealed?"

Paul wrote emphatically: "We are hard pressed on every side, but not crushed; perplexed, but not in despair; persecuted, but not abandoned; struck down, but not destroyed" (2 Cor. 4:8-9).

I want to have a commitment that's pure, don't you? If so, then we need not whine, wither, or faint when we feel the pressure build or the temperature rise.

Read one of my favorite passages, Hebrews 10:38-39. Read it out loud!

If you struggle with being defined by trials and heartaches, this may need to be your new favorite passage. Memorize it. Look in the mirror and speak it to yourself. Don't lose heart. Instead of fainting, have faith. Set your hope on the fact that God will sustain you and strengthen you, no matter what you are facing, no matter what life delivers to your door. These verses encapsule this promise: When we live by faith, we are not destroyed.

Pause to pray. Talk to God about your faith. Tell Him where you're struggling. Ask Him to make this promise come alive to you. Journal your thoughts and feelings.

Today we've seen two inadequate responses to hard times. Two more appropriate responses are available to us, according to Hebrews 12. We'll learn about those tomorrow.

DAY THREE

We Four and No More: Part 2

We've all had occasion to act the part of the fatalist or the fainter. Thankfully, though, none of us must keep these as lifelong roles! Children of the King are neither destined nor designed to shrivel up and die in the midst of heartache. Keep your Bible open to Hebrews 12, and study with me as we discover two correct responses to trouble.

3. The faithful follower

The third response to hardship is faithfulness. In Hebrews 12:7 the writer tells us to "Endure hardship as discipline; God is treating you as sons." Sometimes we read the word *endure* and see the picture of a Christian couch potato—nursing her wounds and letting life come to a full stop. But that's not what this word means.

This isn't a passive, laid-back word at all! The term *endure* in its original language actually means: "1) to remain, i.e., abide, not recede or flee; a) to preserve: under misfortunes and trials, to hold fast to one's faith in Christ; b) to endure, bear bravely and calmly: ill treatments."[2]

Take time to read the following Scriptures. Write the number or letter of the definition above that seems to best fit with the meaning of the verse:

_____ Matthew 10:22   _____ Romans 12:12   _____ James 1:2-3

_____ Matthew 24:13   _____ 1 Corinthians 13:7   _____ James 1:12

_____ Mark 13:13   _____ 2 Timothy 2:12   _____ James 5:11

_____ Romans 2:7   _____ Hebrews 10:32   _____ 1 Peter 2:20

With what you've learned about the meaning of *endure* and *discipline*, write your own version of Hebrews 12:7:

_____

_____

Write it once again; this time, begin with your name to personalize the message. Then, instead of the generic word "hardship," insert the difficulty you are currently experiencing that you referenced in days 1 and 2 this week:

_____
(Your name here)

_____

Endure … persevere … stand firm … stand your ground. These words are proactive, don't-give-up kinds of words! They are the very pictures of faithfulness. And perhaps you've noticed, they echo the antidotes offered to the "frail fainter" in yesterday's study.

Hebrews 12 begins verse 1 with a call to perseverance. This verse reminds me of the story of Beth Anne DeCiantis' attempt to qualify for the 1992 Olympic Trials marathon.

> "No discipline seems pleasant at the time, but painful. Later on, however, it produces a harvest of righteousness and peace for those who have been trained by it."
>
> **Hebrews 12:11.**

A female runner must complete the 26 mile, 385 yard race in less than 2 hours, 45 minutes to compete at the Olympic Trials. Beth started strong but began having trouble around mile 23. She reached the final straight-away with two minutes left to qualify. Two hundred yards from the finish, she stumbled and fell. Dazed, she stayed down for 20 seconds. The crowd yelled, "Get up!" The clock was ticking—less than a minute to go.

Beth Anne staggered to her feet and began walking. Five yards short of the finish, she fell again. She began to crawl, the crowd cheering her on, and crossed the finish line on her hands and knees. Her time? Two hours, 44 minutes, 57 seconds.[3]

Don't throw in the towel or faint. Crawl if you have to. Remain faithful, for a reward beyond imagination awaits you. God promises: "Blessed is the man who perseveres under trial, because when he has stood the test, he will receive the crown of life that God has promised to those who love him" (Jas. 1:12).

4. The fruitful finisher

The last response to the discipline of hardship appears in Hebrews 12:11.

Read Hebrews 12:11 in the margin. Place a star beside the two benefits discipline can produce in your life.

Note that the harvest of righteousness and peace is not an automatic result of enduring the crush of great difficulty. No, only those who have chosen to be "trained" by their affliction will experience a great reward. This is your spiritual workout, the flexing and training of faith's muscles. Like any exercise program, this one needs consistency and commitment for a lifetime. Fruitful finishers know that hardship can produce priceless treasures, but only if we submit to our heavenly Father.

The three Scriptures below describe this well; they each reference an image of God's discipline from day one—either "refining fire," "the potter's hand," or "a father's discipline." Match each of the following Scriptures with the image it best portrays.

Proverbs 3:11-12   refining fire
Isaiah 29:16   potter's hand
1 Peter 1:7   father's discipline

Conclude today by paraphrasing the wonderful summary statement about God's discipline found in Hebrews 12:10:

_____

Record in your journal any prayer God is prompting you to pray about your hardships and His discipline.

DAY ❀ FOUR

Canvas for His Glory

We naturally tend to assume that calamities are punishment for our sins, but we can choose a more biblical perspective. We can see them as a canvas on which the hand of God illustrates the many shades of His grace and glory. You'll see what I mean as you study the ninth chapter of John 9.

Read John 9:1-3. What question did the disciples ask Jesus?

_____

How did Jesus respond to their question?

_____

The disciples weren't wrong to connect sin and human suffering, since all suffering entered the world because of man's fall (Gen. 3:16-19).

The intriguing detail in the disciples' question was their assumption that sin caused blindness. They reflected the thinking of their day; their culture associated great suffering with great sin. *If the man's blindness resulted from his own sin, then when did he sin? He was, after all, born blind!* The rabbis taught that man could sin in the womb, based on the story of Jacob and Esau (see Gen. 25). On the basis of Exodus 20:5, the rabbis also taught that parents' sin could have repercussions for future generations.

Jesus' response jolted His disciples back to reality, " 'It was neither that this man sinned, nor his parents; but it was in order that the works of God might be displayed in him' " (John 9:3, NASB).

Our thinking about suffering is not all that far removed from the disciples of two thousand years ago. Our Lord's answer to His disciples is the very message I often hear whispered in my spiritual ear as God and I have discussed my blindness: "This happened so that the work of God might be displayed in [your] life" (John 9:3). If ever I needed reassurance about God's providential timing in my suffering, this is the story for me—and for you, too. Did you catch the sequence? Jesus said that the man's blindness happened for God's glory *before* He actually healed him. My friends, the work of God is displayed in the heartache—not only in the healing. In other words, God's glory was displayed through the man's blindness before the healing ever happened.

If God is using your difficulty as a canvas for His glory ... (think creatively)

What colors would He use? _____

What subject would He capture? _____

How long would it take to complete His work? _____

What mood would be invoked in those who stood before His finished product?

_____

How would you feel that this moment in your life was captured by Him for others

to see and study? _____

_____

If Jesus had not chosen to heal him, could this blind man still have shown God's glory? If God doesn't remove your heartache or suffering, can your life still be a canvas for His glory?

People marveled at the miracle of this man's restored sight. The healed man himself fumbled for an explanation as the Pharisees confronted him. All he could say was, "One thing I do know. I was blind but now I see!" (John 9:25).

I'm convinced the glory of God can be displayed in my blindness, too—even if God chooses not to show His glory through healing me. Yes, it's an undeniable miracle for blind eyes to see. But God also shows Himself strong in the life of someone who suffers and still remains faithful. It captivates us to see someone confined and constrained by trials and calamity who still bears the fruit of peace and righteousness. That's when we truly see God's glory, because it can only be God fashioning such beauty from the elements of certain despair.

Read Ephesians 2:10. What an amazing statement of our life's beauty and purpose! We are God's workmanship; we are created to serve others whom He also created. Pause to write this verse in your journal and take five minutes to begin memorizing it.

The word *workmanship* is sometimes rendered "handiwork" or "masterpiece." The Greek word is *poiema* (you can see our English word "poem" in it) and it carries the idea of work of art.[4] When God created your life, He wasn't filling a mechanistic, prefabricated work order. He was working with creative inspiration to produce a one-of-a-kind, never-before-seen, original work of art—a masterpiece—you! And all who come across your path will see the distinctive brush strokes of God Himself, recognize His work in your life, and find convincing evidence of a great, glorious, creative God.

Journal a prayer confessing to God anything hiding the masterpiece He is making of your life. How much suffering comes from struggling against your life circumstances? What might happen if you chose to be grateful, every day, for the gift of your life?

DAY ❀ FIVE
Yield to the Touch

Over and over Scripture refers to us as "dust" or "clay" such as in Genesis 2:7, "The LORD God formed the man from the dust of the ground and breathed into his nostrils the breath of life, and the man became a living being." The psalmist reminds us that God "remembers that we are dust" (Ps. 103:14). Paul refers to us as jars of clay (2 Cor. 4:7). In its rudimentary form, clay isn't impressive; but when it's molded by a potter, artfully shaped, and refined by fire, it becomes a work of art.

An earthen vessel acquires its loveliness from the consistent and purposeful pressure of the potter's hand. As we saw in Hebrews, however, that process can be painful. Picture a lump of clay. Plopped on the potter's wheel, it takes its own natural shape—hardly more than an indistinct blob. Then the potter goes to work—pushing, pulling, tugging, molding. As that process continues, he transforms the clay into something lovely and useful.

Making a pot requires three ingredients: the clay, the wheel, and of course, the potter. The potter must think of a project, exert skillful pressure, fashion a vessel, and decide when it's all complete. The wheel must spin steadily and provide momentum. The clay must be still and yield to the potter's touch.

You are that clay, and God is the potter. The spinning wheel represents your life's constantly moving circumstances.

Reflect on the many ways God has touched you. Re-read the weekly Touch Stone verses. Record in your journal how your life circumstances have revealed God's touch on your life.

God takes us into His loving hands and crafts us into something supernatural. That's why we sometimes experience such pain. Let's be real here: the refining touch of God in our lives is not merely uncomfortable; it can also hurt—and hurt deeply. It might require us to bend in ways we never anticipated. It might compel us to yield and stretch in ways we never expected.

Maybe you've been there recently, my friend. Maybe you're there right now. You're wondering how the pain you've been enduring can possibly produce anything other than ruin and ashes in your life. I understand. I've been there, too!

I'll never forget a certain date with Phil, back when we were in college. We'd been dating a little more than a year when one fateful evening he invited me out to dinner. As we sat in the front seat of his old '66 Dodge, he began to tell me something. I could immediately sense that this something was difficult for him to say. "Jennifer, I've noticed something that I need to discuss with you. You are awfully negative."

As he explained what he had observed, my mind was reeling! How dare he! After all, I thought I was in pretty good shape. I wasn't a pessimist. I was a realist. Everyone in his right mind knew the glass was most certainly half empty! Only dewy-eyed Pollyannas went around seeing the glass half full. At that moment, however, the water in my "half-empty glass" was starting to boil. I was furious! I tried to listen as he gently explained my deficiencies. He even gave examples! I argued, justified, and tried to shift the conversation to his faults. What I really wanted to do was dump my half empty glass of water onto his sanctimonious head.

How do you think you would have responded in the same situation?
- ❏ sincere gratefulness: "thanks for helping me to be better."
- ❏ flaming anger: "let me tell you about your faults, big boy."
- ❏ crushed silence: "I thought you cared about me."
- ❏ other: _____

As you can imagine, that date didn't end very well. An Arctic cold front gripped the interior of Philip's Dodge, and we soon called it a night. We temporarily patched things up the next day and moved on, but that conversation haunted me for years. Eventually, many miles down life's road, it finally prodded me to see my own reflection in the half-empty glass. As painful and embarrassing as that front-seat confrontation was, it brought forth something pleasant and fruitful in my life. God used the painful truth of Phil's words to turn my natural pessimism into supernatural optimism.

From the following verses, write down the difficult thing God uses to refine us. Then record the beautiful result of that process.

Proverbs 15:31 _____

James 1:2-4 _____

1 Peter 1:6-7 _____

Sometimes God allows difficult things to come into our lives to refine us. Sometimes He allows us to receive difficult truths so He can correct us and conform us into vessels that radiate His glory.

Read Jeremiah 18:1-4. What happened to the potter's first attempt at making a pot?

_____

How did the potter respond to the marred pot?
- ❏ threw it away and started again
- ❏ added some new clay to improve the results
- ❏ reshaped it into another form
- ❏ forgot the whole thing and took up fishing instead

The following verses speak of our responsibility and God's purposes. How do the verses relate to our role as clay and God's position as the divine potter?

Psalm 46:10 _____

Ecclesiastes 3:11 _____

Romans 9:20-21 _____

Philippians 2:13 _____

We've considered ways God touches us to shape us into His image. Have you felt His merciful touch like a cool shadow on a hot day? His strong hand lift you out of darkness, failure, or despair? The pressure of His fingers shaping you into someone who will reflect His glory?

God's touch shelters, honors, guides, and restores. What you have received, my friend, you can also give. God may choose to use you to touch others within the hour, in the middle of the night, or in a way you never even considered. Yours is the skin He chooses, and yours will be the life He uses.

Ask God to help you be ready to extend His touch whenever and however He chooses to use you.

Touch Point
God has left His fingerprints on your life. Now, offer yourself to others. Your time, a listening ear, carefully chosen words of encouragement, and acts of help and kindness. When you do, you become His touch. Remember, according to Matthew 25:40, when you touch others, you touch God.

[1]"Lexicon Results for *paideia* (Strong's 3809)," Blue Letter Bible [online], [cited 15 October, 2004]. Available from the Internet: www.blueletterbible.org.

[2]"Lexicon Results for *hupomeno* (Strong's 5278)," Blue Letter Bible [online], [cited 15 October, 2004]. Available from the Internet: www.blueletterbible.org.

[3]"Persistence Pays!" Leadership Dynamics [online], 27 April 1998, [cited 15 October, 2004]. Available from the Internet: www.leadershipdynamics.org.

[4]"Lexicon Results for *poiema* (Strong's 4161)," Blue Letter Bible [online], [cited 19 October, 2004]. Available from the Internet: www.blueletterbible.org.

Listening Guide

God uses _____ circumstances in our lives to

_____ us.

God wants to reveal His _____ in the midst of your

_____.

When we find God's hands refining and shaping us, we must _____ ___!

When you can't _____ God's hand, _____ His heart.

Leader Guide

Steps for Leading This Study

Step 1. Begin publicity four weeks before the Introductory Session. Tell whether childcare is provided and if participants will pay for their books.

Step 2. Order member books and the leader kit which provides DVDs.

Step 3. Reserve a meeting room, a TV, a DVD player, and a CD/tape player.

Step 4. Study *Fingerprints of God;* view videos ahead of the group (20-25 minutes each).

Step 5. Enlist an "In Touch" leader to communicate with group members every week and a "Prayer Touch" leader to generate the weekly prayer list and lead the prayer activities mentioned in First Touch. NOTE: Contact these two leaders each week, just as they are contacting and caring for participants.

Step 6. Ask the Holy Spirit to make His presence evident. Praise God for His being the living Word. Confess any sins that hamper growth in your faith. Finally, pray for each woman by name and by need.

First Touch Steps for Every Session

1. Share Touch Point stories from the past week.
2. Prayer Touch leader facilitates prayer time and keeps a prayer list for the group.
3. Design a prayer activity related to these prayer reports and requests.

Introductory Session

Before the Session

1. Provide the registration list to the In Touch Leader to make personal contacts and to the Prayer Touch Leader to pray for members by name.

2. Obtain: modeling clay in various bright colors, large notecards, highlighters, and member books.

3. (Optional. See During the Session, number 7.) Recreate an ancient altar in your meeting room using large rocks or paving stones.

During the Session

1. Welcome the group. Introduce yourself.

2. Invite group to use the modeling clay to spell out their names or make a representation of their names. Provide large notecards for a base for the women to work with the clay and then easily move or display. Offer encouragement. After 5 minutes, ask each member to introduce herself by showing her creation and explaining its details. Enjoy these presentations; affirm efforts.

3. Ask for volunteers who can recall every name in the room. Welcome participants again.

4. Say: *"Fingerprints of God* starts with this basic premise: We are individually touched by God—created by Him, recreated through Jesus Christ, refined and restored through the Holy Spirit. In only a few minutes, we've used our hands to create letters and objects with a lot of meaning attached to them. Our creative efforts brought laughter to the room and forged connections between us. If our creative handiwork in which we've shaped something to represent ourselves could do all that, just imagine what happens when God touches us."

5. Pray a blessing for each person by name and ask for God's guidance for all the sessions ahead.

6. Distribute *Fingerprints of God* to each member. Say: "Let's get acquainted with the features of this study."

7. Direct attention to each week's Touch Stone. Explain that this features a key verse or passage relating to the week's study. Distribute notecards so members can copy week 1's Touch Stones. Encourage members to read the Touch Stones as they start each day's study, to use it as the basis for prayer, to move the card daily like a bookmark, and to memorize the Scripture. **Optional:** Recreate an ancient altar in your meeting room using large rocks or paving stones. Remind members that our spiritual ancestors built altars where they met God, were changed by God, and then worshiped God. Each week write the weekly Touch Stone on a rock. Use the altar for prayer times, for making commitments to God, and for other Scripture activities.

8. Say, "You'll learn what it means to be touched by God as you faithfully engage in this study's daily activities. When we gather together, we'll offer our experiences of study, prayer, and service to encourage and instruct each other."

9. To get acquainted with the workbook, divide into groups of three and find pages 9-10 in week 1, day 1. Have groups read this portion and do all activities together. Allow about 10 minutes.

Call time. Ask the groups to list workbook benefits (see great Bible truths; helps apply Scripture to my life; guides me so I won't miss key truths; provides opportunity to pray, think, journal).

10. Ask members to turn to page 44, week 3, day 2 (begins "When we experience") and to work alone to read this portion and begin activities through page 45. **(Optional:** choose activities that fit in the time you have available or simply discuss the following questions.)

Call time. Discuss: What would you miss if you skip these Scriptures? What would you miss if you don't complete these activities?

Encourage participants to be thorough in their study—to read the book's content, look up all the Scriptures, and complete the study activities.

11. Have members highlight the final paragraph of week 2, day 5 (p. 36) about God's Word.

12. Point out several places where members are instructed to journal. **Ask participants to bring their journals to class.** Remind them they can also use their journals for group prayer requests, recording study notes, or writing out prayers, thoughts, or feelings prompted while they study. It becomes a record of their worship and discipleship.

13. Look at the Contents page and say, "This book begins with the fingerprint, the gentlest touch of all, and leads you into deeper intimacy with God through the images of God's hands, His embrace, and His daily presence. Week by week, you'll rediscover that being touched by God's hand means He is close to you, present with you, cares for you, and chooses you just as you are and just as He's designed you to be."

14. Find the Touch Point at the end of each week. Encourage members to read this daily and to seek to accomplish its goal during the week. Each session includes time for sharing Touch Point stories and prayer concerns. Say: "We'll choose or design one Touch Point activity for our group to do at the study's end. As you do these assignments weekly, look for ideas to suggest."

15. Ask for questions or comments about the study. Reassure members regarding their concerns.

16. Return to groups of three. Ask each member to record her choice of a study time in her own book and to write an encouraging message in the others'.

17. Tell members that each session will conclude with a "Don't Miss!" message which the In Touch leader will reinforce during the week.

18. The "Don't Miss!" for this week is to bring a homemade item for week 1.

19. View the introductory session video.

> **Answers:** character; presence; rescues; comfort; honors; restores; compassionate; personal; leads, guides; lifts; mercy; recognize; receive; extend

20. Replay Jennifer's singing "He Touched Me" from the DVD as your benediction.

Session 1: Fingerprints of God

Before the Session

1. Obtain: washable ink pads; notecards; pins.

During the Session

1. Have members print their names on notecards using inked fingerprints to form the letters, and then pin on nametags.
2. Ask, Can anyone recall every member's name? Share brief descriptions of their homemade items.
3. Discuss: "What makes being homemade special?" Draw parallels between their answers and that God "made us Himself" in creative, redemptive love.
4. Complete the First Touch steps (p. 104).
5. Divide into five groups. Assign each group one day from week 1. Say, "Find the most meaningful Scripture, most inspirational quote, and most effective activity."

Call time after 10 minutes and hear reports. Affirm members' responses and thorough study. Encourage continued thorough study during week 2.
6. Have members highlight the paragraph beginning "Many years have passed ..." (day 2, p. 11) as a volunteer reads it aloud. In their journals, ask members to complete the following:

"I don't feel valuable to God when ..."

"I don't feel noticed by God when ..."

"I don't feel God's touch when ..."

Ask each member to share one completed statement and to work together to find reassurance from the week 1 content and Scriptures for each concern. Suggest members record in their journals the help offered by group members.
7. The "Don't Miss!" for week 2 is the last two paragraphs of week 2, day 2 and the journaling assignment; the final activity of week 2, day 3; and the Touch Point from week 2.
8. View session 1 video, "Fingerprints of God."
   Answers: fashioned; chose, hands; touch; gaze; beauty, honor; Sword

9. Have pairs swap nametags. Ask them to pray for each other daily and to make one phone call encouraging the other to complete the Touch Point task. Allow a moment for pairs to share prayer concerns.
10. Close with prayer.

Session 2: A Touch of Intimacy

Before the Session

1. Obtain: bottled water, permanent markers, a dry erase board, and erasable markers

During the Session

1. Give participants water bottles as they arrive; place markers nearby for writing names on one side and what makes them thirsty on the other. No drinking yet!
2. Instruct them to greet other members by swapping water bottles with one another until you call time. Have participants introduce the person who last swapped with them, giving that person's name and thirsty list from the bottle. Then ask them to return the bottle to its original owner.
3. Link the theme of thirst found throughout week 2 and ask members to drink all their water during today's session. Remind them to consider their spiritual thirst as they quench their physical thirst.
4. Complete the First Touch steps (p. 104).
5. From page 25, ask group to share their responses to the activities about thirst that conclude day 1. Ask participants to describe the effect of the prayer activity. Ask a volunteer to read her written prayer.
6. As a group, record all the biblical people mentioned in week 2 on the dry erase board.
7. Assign names on the board to participant pairs until all names are distributed.
8. Ask pairs to quickly find all mention of their assigned name(s) in week 2 and write a phrase that describes the biblical person's relationship to God.
9. Call time and hear reports. Use the discussion to highlight key truths about the intimate relationship God desires to have with His people.

10. Ask participants to highlight the paragraph on page 31 that begins "When we fix our spiritual eyes …" Remind them that what we most need—are thirsty for—is just what God provides us through Jesus. Review answers in the exercise following that paragraph. Ask partners to share from the next activity (p. 32) which "I AM" statement they chose and why.

11. View the session 2 video, "A Touch of Intimacy."

Answers: longing, known; God; familiarity, intimacy; God, you; reveal, ordinary; God, initiates; heartache

12. Ask partners to exchange empty water bottles and to pray daily for that person and her needs.

13. The "Don't Miss!" for week 3 is careful study of day 1, and making and bringing to session 3 "Gotcha Day" invitations (p. 46).

14. Close with prayer.

Session 3: His Redeeming Touch
Before the Session
1. Carefully study day 1 Scriptures from Romans, Galatians, and Ephesians to guide discussion.
2. Obtain poster-sized paper, large markers, tape, nametags with "Once I Was" printed in the top left corner and "But Now I Am" in the top right corner.

During the Session
1. As members gather, ask them to choose the continuum most meaningful to them (day 2, p. 45) and fill in answers on the nametag.
2. Invite members to share reasons for their choices and a testimony about their Christian experience.
3. Complete the First Touch steps (p. 104).
4. Recall the before and after pictures from pages 40-41. Divide into three groups. Assign group 1 the Romans Scriptures and content in both the before and after sections of day 1. Assign group 2 the Galatians Scriptures and content from both sections, and group 3 the Ephesians Scriptures and content. Give each group markers and two large sheets of paper.

Instruct groups to review content as well as their responses to the exercises and to "picture" the before and after truths. Hear reports from all three groups; display posters on the wall.

5. Ask members to share their drawings of God's seal with their small groups (p. 43). Recall content regarding God's seal at the end of day 4 (p. 51).
6. Invite participants to share their "Gotcha Day" invitations (day 2). Collect invitations in a large bag as they are shared. Conclude with each member drawing out another's invitation as a reminder to pray for that person in the upcoming week.
7. View the session 3 video, "His Redeeming Touch."

Answers: sin, treasure; blood, Christ; mercy

8. The "Don't Miss!" for week 4 is members' studying day 5 until they understand the link between God's protection and their self-control.
9. Close with prayer.

Session 4: His Sheltering Embrace
Before the Session
1. Plan with In Touch and Prayer leaders a group project like one of the Touch Point activities. Consult with appropriate church staff to secure support and resources, if needed.
2. Display the list of storms from page 59.
3. Prepare to discuss idols in Scripture as mentioned in day 3 (for example, What do idols represent? Why does God despise them? Why did people continually build their own idols rather than worship God?).
4. Duplicate the chart from page 65 on a large poster and hang it in an out-of-the-way place.

During the Session
1. As members arrive, ask them to write their answers for the chart (p. 65) onto the large poster.
2. Invite them to the large group. Refer members to the list of storms. Ask them to identify which storm best describes their week and to explain their answers to two other members.

3. Ask: "In a positive sense, which word best describes your experience to date in this study?" (for example: downpour of blessings or a flood of new friends). Ask for answers from the Scripture activity on page 60 and the journal entry prompted at the end of day 1.

4. Complete the First Touch steps (p. 104).

5. Open this session with a prayer using the names of God from page 61.

6. Discuss idols, referring to day 3. Have members highlight the italicized statement on page 64. Discuss the questions concluding day 3.

7. Bring the poster of the day 4 chart into the group circle. Add up marks and invite insights about what the answers reveal about the group.

Discuss the link between the pebbles of day 3 and how much believers rely on God's strength in day 4.

8. Offer a personal example of how you've learned to value self-control as discussed in day 5.

Creatively pair members; assign each pair to call or meet before the next session to discuss week 5, day 5 in detail and to pray for each other; this is the "Don't Miss" for the week.

9. View session 4 video, "His Sheltering Embrace."

Answers: uncomfortable, shelter; protect; preserve; position; character; kneel, healed

10. Close in prayer.

Session 5: The Hand That Guides

Before the Session

1. Meet with other leaders to finalize plans for group's Touch Point activity.

2. Make three displays: one of home repair tools; one of kitchen tools; one of gardening tools.

During the Session

1. In pairs, ask members to choose three tools from any group displayed that represent how God is at work in our lives. Hear reports and affirm answers.

2. Ask and discuss: "What one thing do all these tools have in common?" (Answer: all are held in the hand) Remind group that God's hand guides the process of shaping our lives. Ask for volunteers to share their journal answers from day 1 (p. 75) about times God guided them with His light.

3. Complete the First Touch steps (p. 104).

4. Divide into three groups. Assign each either day 2 (Jonah), 3 (Manasseh), or 4 (Nebuchadnezzar) to discover where they recognize themselves in the main character's story and what tool was in God's hand to guide that person's life (examples: mercy for Jonah; discipline for Manasseh; judgment for Nebuchadnezzar). Call time and hear reports.

5. Review the two tools discussed in day 5—law and repentance. Ask if anyone chose repentance because of her study and God's prompting. Have members highlight the final paragraph of day 5 (p. 86).

6. Return to pairs to discuss how God is shaping their lives through the tools discussed in the session. Instruct pairs to record their partners' needs and prayer requests; have pairs pray together.

7. View session 5 video, "The Hand That Guides."

Answers: liberating; warm, comforting; protective; security; Word; light; Pride, light; Jesus

8. Our "Don't Miss!" for week 6 is to faithfully finish the study this week. Every day is important!

Members will be asked to share the lesson she most needed from week 6 study and how week 6 clarifies how and why God shapes our lives.

9. Close with prayer.

Note to Leaders:

Thank you for leading this study. If you visit www.jenniferrothschild.com/fingerprints, I will send you a CD with the song "He Touched Me" free when you cover a small shipping charge.

Session 6: Shaped by His Hand

Before the Session

1. Finalize plans for your group's Touch Point activity; prepare written directions or instructions group members need to complete it.

2. Ask In Touch leader to remind members of this week's "don't miss" assignment when she makes weekly contacts.

3. Ask Prayer Touch leader to summarize prayer experiences of the study, particularly answered ones.

4. Prepare to give brief summaries of the three images for understanding hardship from day 1, "God's Refining Fire," "God's Shaping Hands," and "God's Fatherly Discipline."

5. Ask In Touch leader to ask someone in the group who is "artsy" to bring in something she has made. This could be a painting, a quilt, a scrapbook, or any other kind of artwork.

During the Session

1. Invite members to view the artwork and name something from the study for which they are grateful. Ask the artist to briefly describe what her project looked like when she began and how she transformed the materials into a work of art. Make application to the idea in day 4 that our lives become a work of art as they display God's glory.

2. Complete the First Touch steps (p. 104).

3. Thank participants for their faithfulness to this group and study.

4. Offer a summary of the three images from day 1, "God's Refining Fire," "God's Shaping Hands," and "God's Fatherly Discipline" (pp. 90-91). With each image, have participants discuss the Scriptures and their responses to the exercises.

5. Note that day 1 ends with a reminder to be grateful. Challenge each participant to continue this practice for at least six more weeks and to journal changes her attitude of gratitude makes in her life.

6. Divide into four groups, assigning each group one of four types of Christians drawn from Hebrews in days 2 and 3—the flippant fatalist, the frail fainter, the faithful follower, and the fruitful finisher. Instruct groups to find one key Scripture and one key sentence from each section. Hear reports; focus discussion on how these two days continue to help us understand our suffering.

7. Hear the Prayer Touch leader's summary. Celebrate God's goodness to the group.

8. Share journal entries from the end of day 4. Use what is shared in a final prayer experience. If possible, pray aloud for each other as you conclude the *Fingerprints of God* study.

9. Ask members to share the lesson they most needed from week 6 study and how week 6 clarifies how and why God shapes our lives.

Encourage the group with what they've learned. Remind them that they bear God's fingerprints, and now they can leave His fingerprints on others' lives!

10. View the session 6 video, "Shaped by His Hand."

Answers: difficult, refine; glory, circumstance; look up; trace, trust

11. The final "Don't Miss!" is contributing to the group project. Hand out instructions as members dismiss. Note: Gather as a group at the project's end for a final time of reviewing the study and sharing its impact on your relationships with God as well as how it will impact relationships with others.

Enjoy the Bible Study?
Now, experience the books.

Fingerprints of God Bible Study is based on

Walking By Faith Bible Study is based on

Fingerprints of God
Recognizing the Touch of God on Your Life

In eight inspiring chapters, Jennifer Rothschild helps readers see God's fingerprints. Rothschild explains that "even more vital than human touch is the touch of God." His touch is not skin on skin, but it's just as real. It warms the heart and shelters the soul. His touch leads the way through darkness.

ISBN 1-59052-530-2

Lessons I Learned in the Dark
Steps to Walking by Faith, Not by Sight

"Believing is seeing" is one of the most important lessons God has taught Jennifer Rothschild since a retinal disease began claiming her eyesight more than 20 years ago. With warmth and humor, she shares the guiding principles she walks by and shows you how too. "*Lessons I Learned in the Dark* is gripping. I don't know the person to whom it has nothing to say." — Beth Moore

ISBN 1-59052-047-5